Giovanni Bottesini (1821-1889)
Alfredo Piatti (1822-1901)
Vincenzo Bellini (1801-1835)

Fantasia

sopra motivi dell'Opera

I Puritani
(Bellini)

Duetto per Violoncello e Contrabbasso

Urtext Edition by Stephen Street
in consultation with Adrian Bradbury and
Chris West

www.bottesiniurtext.com

Edition Copyright 2021 © Stephen Street
Part of the Bottesini Urtext® www.bottesiniurtext.com

Foreword
By Adrian Bradbury

On Boxing Day 1835 Bellini's final opera *I puritani* - "the rage of Paris" following its triumphant premiere there in January that year - opened at La Scala, Milan, just three months on from Bellini's untimely death. That Winter Alfredo Piatti (1822-1901) and Giovanni Bottesini (1821-1889), classmates at the nearby Milan Conservatory, were both turning 14 years of age.

By 1847 each player was famous for his unsurpassed virtuosity - Bottesini the 'Paganini of the double bass' and Piatti the 'Prince of cellists' - but geographically they were an ocean apart, Bottesini on an extended tour (with another Milan Conservatory classmate, violinist Luigi Arditi) of the New World, including Havana and New York, and Piatti in London.

The mid-nineteenth century was an era in which virtuosi would enchant their audiences with 'operatic fantasies', compositions of their own in which arias from a well-known opera were played to show off an instrumental cantabile before being elaborated into technically dazzling variations with an extended finale. *I puritani*, with arias that were 'Top of the Pops' across Europe and the New World, was ideal operatic fantasy material, and so it was that Arditi, Bottesini and Piatti all added to their repertoire, Arditi and Bottesini collaborating to compose a 'Gran Duet on Airs from the Opera *I puritani* for Violin and Double-Bass' (premiered in New York on 12 June 1848, now presumed lost) and Piatti composing his own 'Souvenir des *Puritani*' for cello (his opus 9, premiered in his native Bergamo at a benefit concert on 9 January 1847 to raise money for his forthcoming voyage to London).

Bottesini's arrival on English soil in 1849 saw him reunited with Piatti, a musical partnership that was to delight London audiences for years to come, for instance in chamber concerts for the Musical Union, Chappell's 'Popular Concerts' and as principal players with the Royal Italian Opera, Covent Garden. Together they composed the new work presented in this edition, 'Fantasia sopra motivi dell'opera *I puritani*' for cello and double bass with orchestral accompaniment, perhaps based on the above-mentioned 'Gran Duet' by Arditi and Bottesini but certainly unrelated to Piatti's opus 9. Its first known performance was at a concert promoted by violinist Heinrich Wilhelm Ernst at the Hanover Square Rooms on the 2nd June 1851, after which the Musical World wrote:

"A duetto for violoncello and contra basso, by the two lion performers, Piatti and Bottesini, created a *furore*. It was as though - to depart from our *lion* metaphor - a rhinoceros contended with an elephant, and neither could obtain the mastery. Such an instrumental trial of strength was perhaps never before witnessed. Had Paganini come to life, and fiddle in hand encountered Ernst, the struggle for priority could scarcely have excited more interest, or created more applause. Each artist was on his metal, and surpassed himself. Italian art was never made more manifest, or rendered more triumphant than on this occasion. To describe the performance is impossible; to describe the effect on the audience is equally impossible. Not dealing in impossibilities we shall attempt neither, but consign both to the imagination of our readers."

Further London outings of the work took place later that year at the Musical Union (24th June) and at Jullien's Promenade Concerts (19th and 21st November). Then on 29th March 1852 they performed it for the Philharmonic Society, again at the Hanover Square Rooms, under the baton of compatriot Michael Costa and in the presence of Queen Victoria. *I puritani* - or "dear Puritani!" as she called it - was the Queen's favourite opera, the first she had attended with Prince Albert before their marriage, and she wrote in her journal that night: "a Concertante between Piatti and Bottesini was wonderful and beautifully played." Her evident delight emboldened Piatti to seek, and obtain, her immediate patronage of his "Quartet Association", a chamber music series guaranteeing a 'London premiere' in every concert. By 1858 Bottesini was performing a version of the work for solo double bass and orchestra, in a concert tour (including Verona and Milan) celebrating his first Italian summer since leaving for Havana twelve years previously.

The opera *I puritani* is set in Plymouth against the backdrop of the 1640's English Civil War, and concerns the wedding between Elvira (a Puritan) and Arturo (a Royalist), Elvira's father having been dissuaded from making her marry Riccardo, a Puritan suitor. During the celebrations Arturo discovers that Queen Enrichetta (the widow of Charles I) is imprisoned in the castle, so he quick-wittedly disguises her in the wedding veil and helps her to escape. Elvira, thinking she has been abandoned, loses her mind. Eventually Arturo returns to be joyously reunited with Elvira, only to learn that he is under sentence of death for his actions; but all is soon well again with the news that Oliver Cromwell has pardoned him.

After an orchestral (or piano) introduction, taken from the orchestral opening of the opera, and a short duo cadenza [bar 53], Piatti and Bottesini together present the Act 1 tenor aria '*A te, o cara*' [bar 56] in which Arturo sings of his love for Elvira. A short orchestral (or piano) interlude [bar 81] - the music here taken from the Act 1 chorus '*A festa*' in which the villagers and soldiers celebrate the news of Elvira's forthcoming wedding - then leads into Piatti and Bottesini sharing a rendition of the Act 3 duet "*Nel mirarti un solo istante*" [bar 94] in which Elvira and an apologetic Arturo are reunited. Following solo variations on this number by each player, '*A festa*' is presented once more [bar 154], this time shared between our soloists, from which they segue into the Act 1 baritone aria '*Bel sogno beato*' [bar 194] in which Riccardo despairs in his unrequited love for Elvira. Another cadenza [bar 250] and extended coda of the composers' own invention brings the duo concertante to a virtuoso conclusion.

Adrian Bradbury 2021

A Note On This Publication

This publication has only been possible thanks to the generous support of Stanford University in giving access to Bottesini's autograph manuscript, which they hold in their special collections and which was donated to them by Natale Gallini, a Italian musicologist. I would also like to acknowledge their generosity in giving the Bottesini Urtext® project permission to publish their photographs in this edition, helping to protect the score for future generations. Bottesini's autograph manuscript can be found here:

Stanford Libraries, Department of Special Collections, Memorial Library of Music, MLM 126

Secondly, I could not have asked for a better team of editors to help me on this project. I am very fortunate to have had two of the world's leading authorities on both Piatti and Bottesini helping with this edition. A special thanks goes to both Adrian Bradbury and Chris West for being there to research, proofread and bounce ideas around, producing the best edition we can given all the information found to date. Together with the late Oliver Davies, and in consultation with Dr Annalisa Barzanò of the *Associazione Alfredo Piatti* in Bergamo, Adrian (www.adrianbradburycello.com) has researched and recorded all of Piatti's Operatic Fantasies on the Meridian label (CDE 84642 and 84659), most of these being world premiere recordings. In 2021 Chris West released a revolutionary biography on Bottesini's life, *The Paganini of the Double Bass*, which this publication was involved as part of Chris' research. Chris' book can be found on amazon and through his website (https://www.chriswestbass.com) and his brilliant new book contains many new discoveries into Bottesini's life, dispelling many perpetuated inaccuracies.

This project has entailed digitising, type setting and drawing together a considerable amount of information. From this work, we have created an informed edition of *I Puritani* based around six primary sources:

1. Bottesini's autograph score for cello, double bass and orchestra (1851)
2. Bottesini's autograph score for double bass and piano (1858)
3. Bottesini's orchestral accompaniment parts from his collection of scores, written for double bass and orchestra (dated 1879 in Rio de Janeiro by one of the players performing, but most likely used before this)
4. Vincenzo Ottomano's copy of Bottesini's score for cello and double bass (1897)
5. Mark Starr's edition (1980)
6. An early score of the opera (1830's)

Any edits or information that has been brought into this edition of *I Puritani* from another source has been listed for the performer to reference. Within the Urtext score, an asterisk links to this list. Within the soloist's part of the Urtext edition, any markings taken from Bottesini's edition for solo double bass and piano have been shown on the underside of the stave. The use of dashed slurs, brackets or asterisks indicates any other differences that have been included from other sources. All this information is contained within the edit-marking sheet.

Alongside the Urtext edition, this publication contains a performer's critical edition which is easy to read and combines all the information taken from the various sources. The orchestration has been made fit for the modern orchestra with new parts for brass with valves: the edition contains new parts for French horns in F and trumpets in Bb, and replaces the serpent with the bass trombone. There is also an alternative part for clarinet in Bb, rather than A, and for timpani as a non-transposing instrument. In addition, orchestral clash cymbals could double the bass drum part at forte moments in this piece.

It is important to note that both the original instrumentation and the modern performer's edition are contained in the parts, giving the option to perform this both as with a period orchestra as a historically-informed performance, or with an orchestra with today's instrumentation.

The performer's critical edition also contains occasional minor edits in order to iron out inconsistencies of dynamics or slurring. These are all based on research conducted across the sources, and by becoming increasingly accustomed to how Bottesini wrote shorthand within his own scores.

To go along with the Urtext and performer's editions with orchestral accompaniment, I have constructed a 'new' piano accompaniment from Bottesini's own manuscripts. Unfortunately, a piano reduction for the I Puritani Duetto for cello and contrabbasso is unable to be found; however, Bottesini did write a piano reduction for the version for double bass and piano accompaniment. To stay as authentic as possible to Bottesini's intentions, it made perfect sense to reconstruct a piano reduction from the solo edition. I combined this later edition with the Duetto, reducing the orchestral accompaniment to piano and using this to fill the gaps where the structure differed in the later edition. Many of the melody lines that had previously been performed on the cello had been written into the right hand of the piano, and those therefore had to be removed to accompany the Duetto version.

Note: I have not included any asterisks in the piano reduction as it is constructed from both the Duetto score and from the edition for double bass and piano. As it is constructed from two of Bottesini's manuscript sources and did not exist originally as one complete score, it does not profess to be Urtext.

Names of the themes used in this piece have been added to all versions of this publication to help the performer reference Bellini's original opera. It's apparent from Bottesini's longer phrase marks and *piu mosso* markings in other manuscripts that perhaps the tempo's of some of the variations are a little brisker than had been thought previously.

In bars 64-79 of the Double Bass Soloist, Bottesini leaves out extra flags on stems in the solo double bass and solo cello lines in the manuscript. This is most likely as a minor mistake, probably caused by writing quickly and the use of shorthand, and was confirmed by checking against the manuscript of the later solo double bass version where the flags *are* present.

Bottesini uses repeat marks many times in this score, and I have tried to stay true to them where possible. I have only written occasional bars out where I thought it was best to avoid confusion.

Within the main cadenza, Bottesini's markings for arco and pizzicato in the solo double bass part could perhaps cause a little confusion. A third of the way into the cadenza, Bottesini writes a pizzicato marking. With the location of this marking below the stave (rather than above as usual) being so close to the repeated bottom note, and with the repeated lower note having its own articulation, I believe it only applies to these four repeated E naturals (the sounding pitch written in the score), and not to the upper line. This also makes sense for the rest of the cadenza that follows, considering the slurring and speed of the notes that would not sound appropriate if plucked. I have marked in the score the changes between pizzicato and arco with an asterisk so that the performer can make their own choice.

I hope that you enjoy performing this piece!

Stephen Street

KEY

*= A difference between the modern edition and the manuscript. Please refer to the manuscript.

If a single slash is used / it equals repeat the beat before it.

If a single slash with dots either side - it means repeat the whole bar.

If a double slash or more is used, the number of slashes dictate the numbers of bars to be repeated. The number of bars to be repeated are usually written above the marking.

If any mistakes are found please get in contact through the Bottesini Urtext website at - www.bottesiniurtext.com so that changes can be put into future prints.

Terms and conditions - by downloading/purchasing/obtaining a copy (by any means) of this edition you are accepting the right to rehearse this edition only. To perform, record or stream using this edition please make a donation to the Bottesini Urtext project or discuss rights by contacting them through www.bottesiniurtext.com to help support the creation of further resources and the protection of Bottesini's music for generations to come.

All rights to this publication belong to Stephen Street and the Bottesini Urtext® project. No part of this publication maybe copied, shared or distributed without permission. For all rights enquiries please get in contact through the Bottesini Urtext website - www.bottesiniurtext.com.

List of Edits

Bar Number	Instrument/Instruments effected	Change Made
	*Solo edition refers to Bottesini's manuscripts (both piano and orchestral accompaniment) of the later edition arranged for solo double bass and not as a duet*	
1-16	Brass and Strings	Accents were only added for the first two bars in the Bass and Cello part. The solo bass orchestral version contains accents for strings and brass for the first 16 bars, however staccatos in Bottesini's piano manuscript for solo bass. Accents have been added to unify the accents already written and the later solo orchestral parts.
3	Bassoons	2nd Bassoon corrected wrong note
9	All	Crescendo added from Bottesini's solo bass edition
17-23	Strings	Staccato's added from Bottesini's solo bass edition
23 (a)	All	Bellini's score has empty bars before the timpani roll enters. It is upto the player if they would like to add a bars silence to make it more like bellini's original score. This also makes it an eight bar phrase to the next entry. Bottesini comes straight in with no break, making a seven bar phrase.
29	Cello	Added missing arco marking
30	Oboe, Clarinet, Bassoons, Corni (la)	Piano dynamic added to match other players, as suggested by the score
38	Oboe, Clarinet, Bassoons, Corni (mi)	Piano dynamic added to
38	Clarinet	Missing accidental added
39	Oboe	Missing accidental added
40	Corni + Strings	Piano dynamic added from Bottesini's Solo bass edition
41	Flute + Violin 1	Piano dynamic added to match other markings
42	Double Bass	Accent Added to match other accents in the same bar
44	Double Bass	Accent Added to match other accents in the same bar
48	Strings	Added missing fortissimo marking
52	Cello Soloist	Slur added to match Double Bass Soloist
52	Cello Soloist	Missing accidental added
52	Double Bass Soloist	Missing accidental added
53	Cello Soloist	Slur added to match Double Bass Soloist
53	Cello Soloist	Missing accidental added
53	Double Bass Soloist	Missing accidentals added
54	Cello Soloist	Missing accidental added
54	Cello Soloist	Piano dynamic marking added to match the double bass soloist
56	Cello Soloist	Missing slur over first three beats of the bar added. Tie between A added. Both added from Bottesini's solo edition
57	Cello Soloist	Slurs and crescendo added from Bottesini's solo bass edition
58	Cello Soloist	Slur added from Bottesini's solo bass edition
59	Cello Soloist	Added missing tie
60	Cello Soloist	slurings shown from different editions (later dotted slurs are prefered)
61	Cello Soloist	Slur added from Bottesini's solo bass edition
61	Cello and Double Bass Soloists	Crescendo added from Bottesini's solo bass edition
62	Cello and Double Bass Soloists	Slurs, accents, performance direction added from Bottesini's solo Bass edition

List of Edits

Bar Number	Instrument/Instruments effected	Change Made
63-80	Double Bass Soloist	Missing beam added. Bottesini accidentally left out the beam that makes it a hemidemisemiquaver repeatedly in the solo bass part, instead he wrote a demisemiquaver which meant that it would not fit in the bar. This is corrected in the later solo edition for double bass and has been corrected in this edition.
63	Cello Soloist	Bottesini accdientally started writing out the beggining of the next bar but quickly ran out of space and so accidentally made a bar of 15/8. He forgot to cross the last beat out. This bar has been corrected in this edition. Its clear it was an accident as the same notes start the next bar and the later solo edition contains what is written in this edition.
63	Strings	Piano dynamic added from Bottesini's Solo bass edition
64	Cello Soloist	Crescendo added from Bottesini's solo bass edition
65/66	Cello Soloist	Slurs added from Bottesini's solo bass edition
67	Cello Soloist	Slur from Solo edition on first beat. Sluring 6 then 3 unified later in the bar. Animando marking from Solo edition
67	Double Bass Soloist	Slur from Solo edition, Animando marking from Solo edition, Cresc from solo edition.
67	Strings	Animando marking from Bottesini's solo edition
67-71	Cello Soloist	Bowing 6 and then 3 unified in bars 67-71
68	Double Bass Soloist	Slurs from Bottesini's later solo edition
68	Strings	Accent added from later solo bass edition
69	Strings + Double Bass Soloist	Crescendo added from Bottesini's solo bass edition
70	Clarinet	Articulations taken from Bottesini's solo bass edition
70	Double Bass Soloist	Slurrings taken from Bottesini's solo bass edition
71	All	colla parte marking taken from solo bass edition
71	Double Bass Soloist	Slurrings and dynamics taken from solo bass edition
74	Strings	Dynamics taken from Bottesini's solo bass edition
75	Clarinet	Slurs added to match flute
76	Flute	Missing slur added, plus missing accidental added
76	Oboe	Missing accidental added
76	Strings	dynamic added from Bottesini's solo bass edition
77	Cello Soloist	Missing accidental added plus dyamic added from Solo Bass edition
78	All	Poco rall added from solo bass edition
78	Strings	dynamic added from Bottesini's solo bass edition
79	Cello and Double Bass Soloists	dynamic added from Bottesini's solo bass edition
80	Strings	Piano dynamic added to match woodwinds
81	Piccolo and flute	Staccato's added from Bottesini's solo bass edition
83	Oboe	Missing accidental added
85	Piccolo and flute	Staccato's added from Bottesini's solo bass edition
87	Clarinet	Missing Fe (forte) marking added
87 - 89	Brass and Bassoon	Accents added from Bottesini's solo Bass edition
89	Viola+cello	Missing piano dynamic added
90	Corni la	Bars written out rather than using repeat marks
91	Violin 1 + 2	Sf accent taken from Bottesini's solo bass edition
92	Strings , Corni la + Bassoons	Calando marking added from solo bass edition
93	double bass soloist	Espressivo marking taken from solo bass edition
93	Violin 2, Cello and Double Bass	Piano marking added to match violins

List of Edits

Bar Number	Instrument/Instruments effected	Change Made
93-95	Double Bass Soloist	Dotted Slurring + articulations taken from Bottesini's solo bass edition
94/97/98/99/100	Violin 1 + 2	Second half of the bar written out avoiding using repeat marks
96	Cello Soloist	Dotted Slurring + articulations taken from Bottesini's solo bass edition
97	Cello Soloist	Slurrings taken from Bottesini's solo bass edition + grace notes taken from solo Bass edition
98	Cello Soloist	Dotted Slurring + articulations taken from Bottesini's solo bass edition
99	Cello Soloist	Slurrings taken from Bottesini's solo bass edition + grace notes taken from solo Bass edition
100	Cello and Double Bass Soloists	Dotted Slurring + articulations taken from Bottesini's solo bass edition
100	Strings	Crescendo added from Bottesini's solo bass edition
100	Cello	Missing arco marking added
100	Cello and Double Bass Soloists	ambandosi marking taken from Rossini's score
100 - 103	Double Bass Soloist	Dotted Slurring + articulations taken from Bottesini's solo bass edition + crescendo
103	Cello Soloist	Crescendo added from Bottesini's solo bass edition
104	Cello Soloist	Missing accidental added plus dyamic added from Solo Bass edition
104	Violin 2	Second half of the bar written out avoiding using repeat marks
105/106	Cello and Double Bass Soloists	Dotted slurring + articulations taken from Bottesini's solo edition
107	All	Poco piu added from Bottesini's solo bass edition
107	Strings	Piano added to all staves as suggested in score
108-110	Cello and Double Bass	Staccato's added from Bottesini's solo bass edition
111	Cello Soloist	Slurring clarified
111	Cello and Double Bass	Staccato's added from Bottesini's solo bass edition
112	Cello and Double Bass	sim marking added
116	Strings	Accent and dynamic marking taken from Bottesini's Solo edition
118	Strings	Accent and dynamic marking taken from Bottesini's Solo edition
119	Cello and Bass	Bars written out rather than using repeat marks
120	Violin 1 + 2/Viola	Bars written out rather than using repeat marks
122	Violin 2	Second half of the bar written out avoiding using repeat marks
123	Violin 1 + 2/Viola	Bars written out rather than using repeat marks
124	Strings	Crescendo added from Bottesini's solo bass edition
125	Violin 1 + Viola	Bars written out rather than using repeat marks
126	Violin 1+2/Viola	Beam split from original score to avoid confusion
126	Double Bass Soloist	fe. dynamic taken from Bottesini's Solo edition
127	Strings	dynamic added from Bottesini's solo bass edition
127/128	Cello and Bass	Articulations taken from Bottesini's solo bass edition
129	Cello and Bass	sim marking added
129	Violin 1+2/Viola	Bar written out rather than using repeat marks
129	Double Bass Soloist	Slurring taken from Bottesini's solo edition
133	Violin 1+2	Bar written out rather than using repeat marks
133	Double Bass Soloist	Slurring taken from Bottesini's solo edition
134	Double Bass Soloist	Slurring taken from Bottesini's solo edition
135	Strings	Accent and dynamic marking taken from Bottesini's Solo edition

List of Edits

Bar Number	Instrument/Instruments effected	Change Made
136	Double Bass Soloist	Slurring taken from Bottesini's solo edition
137	Strings	Accent and dynamic marking taken from Bottesini's Solo edition
137	Double Bass Soloist + Tutti Cello/Bass	Missing accidental added
139	Violin 1+2/Viola	Bar written out rather than using repeat marks
141	Violin 1+2/Viola	Bar written out rather than using repeat marks
143	Strings	dynamic added from Bottesini's solo bass edition
144	Violin 1+2/Viola	Bar written out rather than using repeat marks
146	Strings	Intended dynamics added to all strings
150	Tutti Cello	Bar written out rather than using repeat marks
153	Piccolo and flute	Bar written out rather than using repeat marks
154	Clarinet + Bassoon + Trombone	Bar written out rather than using repeat marks
153/154	Strings	Accents added from Bottesini's solo Bass edition
155/156	Cello Soloist	Dynamics taken from Bottesini's solo bass edition
158	Cello Soloist	Missing passing note added from Bottesini's edition for Solo Bass
157	Violin 1 + 2	Slurring added from Bottesini's edition for Solo Bass
157	Viola/Cello/Bass	Missing dynamics added
158	Strings	Slurring and Dynamics taken from Bottesini's Edition for Solo Bass
159	Violin 1 + 2	Slurring added from Bottesini's edition for Solo Bass
160	Violin 1 + 2	sim marking added + whole bar written out rather than using repeat marks
161	Violin 1 + 2	Bar written out rather than using repeat marks + Dynamics added from Bottesini's edition for solo Bass
161	Violin 1 + 2	Accent taken from Bottesini's Solo edition + Bar Written out rather than using repeat marks
162	Violin 1 + 2	Accent taken from Bottesini's Solo edition + Bar Written out rather than using repeat marks
163	Double Bass Soloist	Missing clef added
164	Cello + Double Bass Soloists	Dynamics taken from Bottesini's solo bass edition
164	Violin 1 + 2	Bar written out rather than using repeat marks + Dynamics added from Bottesini's edition for solo Bass
165	Cello Soloist + Strings	Dynamics taken from Bottesini's solo bass edition
165	Violin 2 + Viola	Bar written out rather than using repeat marks
165/166/167	Viola	Bowing taken from Bottesini Solo Bass Edition + Sim marking added
167	Strings	Dynamics taken from Bottesini's solo bass edition
168	Violin 1 + 2 + Viola	Bar written out rather than using repeat markings + dynamics taken from Bottesini's edition for solo bass
169	Double Bass Soloist + Strings	Crescendo added from Bottesini's solo bass edition
169	Tutti Cello	Missing dynamics added
170	Violin 1 + Viola	Bar written out rather than using repeat marks
170	Tutti Cello + Bass	dynamic added from Bottesini's solo bass edition
171	Double Bass soloist	dynamic added from Bottesini's solo bass edition
171	Strings	Dynamic taken from Bottesini edition for solo bass
171	Clarinet + Corni (trumpet)	Missing crescendo added
172	Violin 1 + 2 + Viola	Accents added from Bottesini's solo Bass edition
172	Violin 1	Bar written out rather than using repeat marks

List of Edits

Bar Number	Instrument/Instruments effected	Change Made
172	Cello Soloist	Dynamic taken from Bottesini edition for solo bass
173/174/175	Strings	Accents taken from Bottesini's edition for Solo Bass
173	Cello Soloist	Slurring taken from Bottesini's solo edition
174	Double Bass + Cello Soloists	Slurring taken from Bottesini's solo edition
175	Double Bass Soloist	Slurring added to match Cello soloist's bowing
176/177	Cello + Double Bass Soloists + Strings	Dynamics taken from Bottesini's solo bass edition
176	Bassoons	Missing dynamics added
177	Tutti	Ritardando marking taken from Bottesini's edition for Solo Bass
178	Tutti	Poco piu/Piu mosso + a tempo added from Bottesini's solo bass edition
183	Cello + Double Bass Soloists	Crescendo added from Bottesini's solo bass edition
184	Clarinets	Slur added to match Bassoons
185	Cello + Double Bass Soloists	Crescendo added from Bottesini's solo bass edition
185/186	Tutti Cello	Missing accidentals added
186	Clarinets	Slur added to match Bassoons
187	Cello + Double Bass Soloists	Crescendo added from Bottesini's solo bass edition
187	Double Bass Soloist	Missing accidental added
187	Strings	Intended dynamics added to all strings
193	Tutti	Piu marking added from Bottesini solo bass edition
193	Cello + Double Bass Soloists + Strings	Dynamics taken from Bottesini's solo bass edition
193	Tutti Cello + Bass	Missing accidentals added
193	Cello + Double Bass Soloists	Phrase mark added from Bottesini's edition for solo bass
193-196	Viola	Bowing clarified/unified from markings used a few bars later in the viola score
194	Double Bass Soloist	Slur added to match Cello soloist
195	Tutti Cello + Bass	Missing accidentals added
197	Double Bass Soloist	Slur added to grace notes
197	Cello Soloist	Grace note beams matched as semi quavers
199	Cello + Double Bass Soloists	Rythm + slurring clarified to match both soloists
199/202/204	Cello + Double Bass Soloists	Bottesini's short hand suggests the bar is slurred in the Cello line and the tie shown in the Double Bass
201/202	Cello + Double Bass Soloists	Dynamics + Slurring taken from Bottesini's edition for solo bass
202	Strings	Intended dynamics added to all strings
203	Strings	Dynamics taken from Bottesini's solo bass edition
204	Cello + Double Bass Soloists	Rythm + slurring clarified to match both soloists
204	Strings	Dynamics taken from Bottesini's solo bass edition
205	Strings	Intended dynamics added to all strings
205	Cello + Double Bass Soloists	Rythm/Sluring on grace notes clarified to match both soloists
205	Tutti cello + Bass	Missing accidental added
207	Cello + Double Bass Soloists	Missing slur added
210	Cello soloist	Missing accidental and slur added
211	Cello Soloist	Tie added
211/212	Double Bass Soloist	Missing accidental added
215	Double Bass Soloist	Missing accidental added
218	Tutti Cello	Intended dynamics added

List of Edits

Bar Number	Instrument/Instruments effected	Change Made
224/225/226	Violin 1 + Violin 2 + Viola	Slurring clarified
227	Tutti Bass	Piano Dynamic added
237	Double Bass Soloist	Slurring and Dynamics taken from Bottesini's Edition for Solo Bass
239	Tutti	Diminuendo marking taken from Bottesini's edition for Solo Bass
239	Cello + Double Bass Soloists	Slurrings taken from Bottesini's edition for Solo Bass
241	Tutti Strings + Double Bass soloist	Dynamics taken from Bottesini's solo bass edition
242	Double Bass Soloist	Dynamic taken from Bottesini edition for solo bass
243	Tutti Strings + Double Bass soloist	Dynamic taken from Bottesini edition for solo bass
244	Tutti Strings + Double Bass soloist	Crescendo added from Bottesini's solo bass edition
244	Double Bass Soloist	Slurring taken from Bottesini's solo edition
245	Double Bass Soloist	Dynamic taken from Bottesini edition for solo bass
245/246	Cello Soloist	Bar written out rather than using repeat marks
246	Violin 2	Bar written out rather than using repeat marks
247	Cello Soloist	Missing Tenor Clef Added
247	Cello + Double Bass Soloist	Crescendo added from Bottesini's solo bass edition
249	Tutti Strings	Dynamic taken from Bottesini edition for solo bass
250 (Cadenza)	Cello Soloist	Ties and Slurring made to Match Double Bass Part + Previous Bar
250 (Cadenza)	Cello Soloist	Octave marking added as harmonic marking makes it sound two octaves higher
250 (Cadenza)	Double Bass Soloist	Missing Bass Clef Added
251 (Cadenza)	Double Bass Soloist	Pizzicato marking suggests it only applies to the lower notes in this bar. Arco for upper notes, pizzicato for lower notes. Alternatively this bar could all be played pizzicato
252 (Cadenza)	Double Bass Soloist	Missing arco marking added
252 (Cadenza)	Double Bass Soloist	Missing pause added to bass part to match cello.
253 (Cadenza)	Double Bass Soloist	Missing accidental added
256 (Cadenza)	Doubl Bass Soloist	Slurs added to match Cello Soloist
261	Cello Soloist	Missing accidental added
269	Cello Soloist	Missing accidental added
270	Cello Soloist	Missing accidental added
271	Violin 1 + 2	Missing pizzicato marking added
271	Cello + Double Bass Soloists	Slurring unified between for Cello + Double Bass Soloists
272-274	Cello Soloist	Bars written out rather than using repeat short hand markings
273/274	Cello Soloist	Missing accidentals added
275/276	Double Bass soloist	Slurring made to match previous markings
276	Tutti Cello + Bass	Missing staccato marking added
277/278	Cello Soloist	Bar written out rather than using shorthand marking
279/280	Double Bass soloist	Slurring made to match previous markings
280	Tutti Viola + Cello	Missing staccato marking added
284	Bassoons	Missing dynamic added
284 - 291	Cello Soloist	Slurring clarified
289	Bassoons	Missing Accidental added
300	Bassoons	SF dynamic added to match horn entry
300	Flute + Oboe	MF dynamic added to match strings
300	Double Bass Soloist	Slur removed to make both notes playable

List of Edits

Bar Number	Instrument/Instruments effected	Change Made
301	Bassoons and Horns 1+2	MF dynamic added to match strings
301	Double Bass Soloist	Missing accidental added
302/303	Clarinet + Horn 3+4	MF dynamic added to match strings
303	Cello Soloist	Missing Accidental added
305	Double Bass Soloist	Notes corrected to fit chord
306	Corni in Mi/ Horns	Bar written out rather than using repeat mark
312	Oboe + all brass	Bar written out rather than using repeat mark
312	Cello Soloist	Missing clef added + Note correction of middle note from D to E
312/313	Double Bass Soloist	Lower note corrected

Edition Copyright 2021 © Stephen Street
Part of the Bottesini Urtext® www.bottesiniurtext.com

Contents

Autograph Manuscript - Page 1

Urtext Edition Full Score - Page 43

Performer's Critical Edition
(with modern instrumentation)
Full Score - Page 99

Giovanni Bottesini (1821-1889)
Alfredo Piatti (1822-1901)
Vincenzo Bellini (1801-1835)

Fantasia

sopra motivi dell'Opera

I Puritani
(Bellini)

Duetto per Violoncello e Contrabbasso

Autograph Manuscript

Courtesy of - Stanford Libraries Department of Special Collections

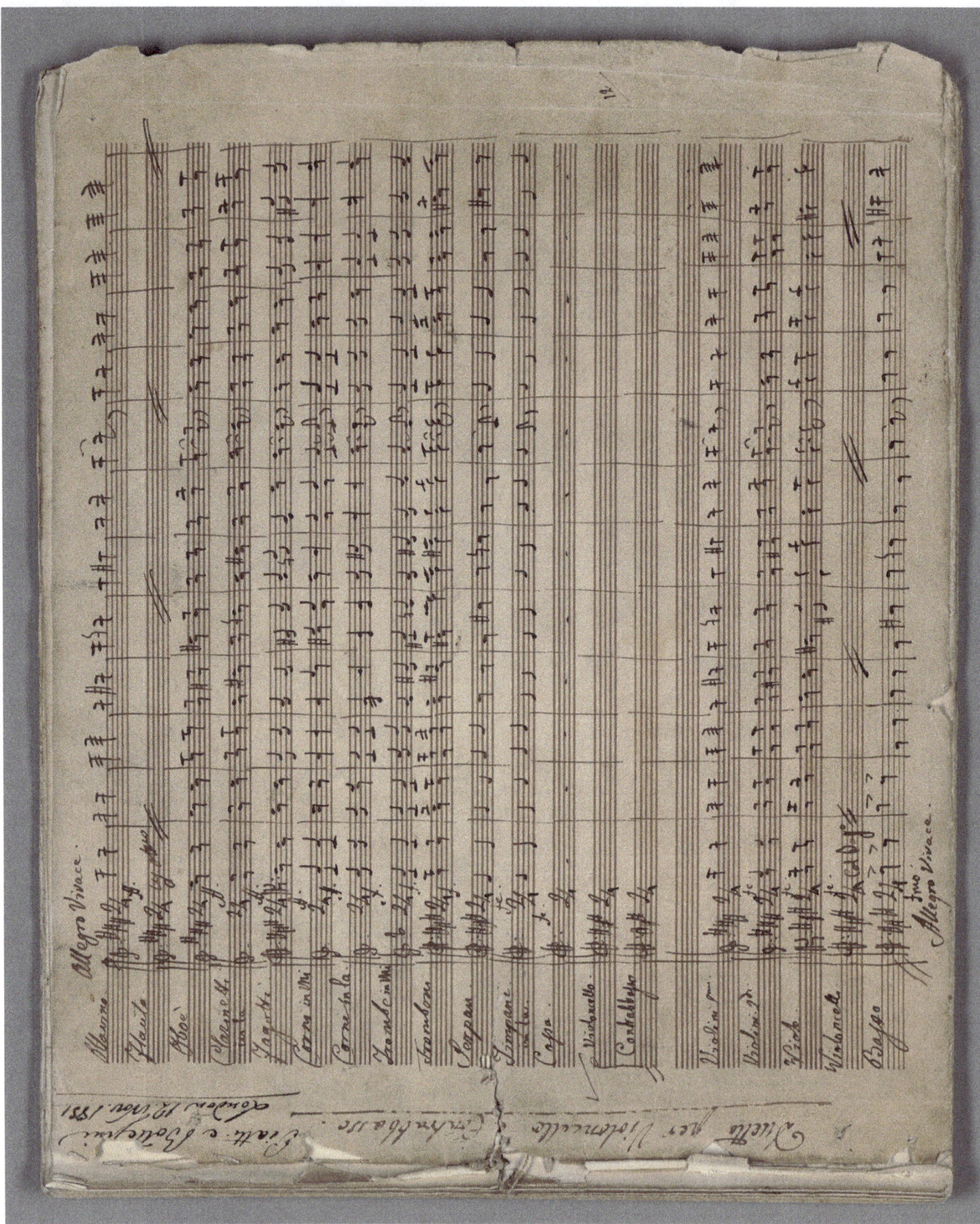

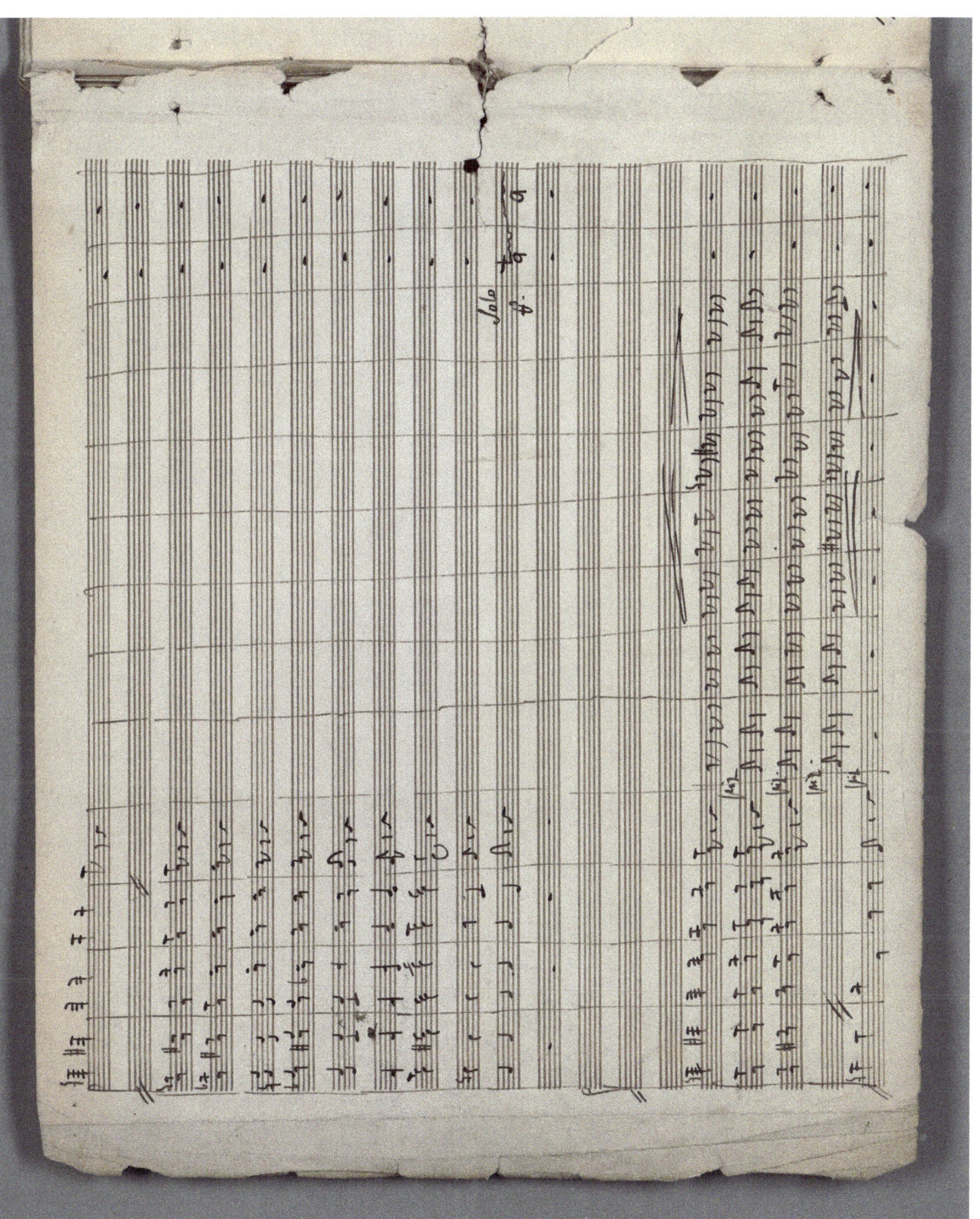

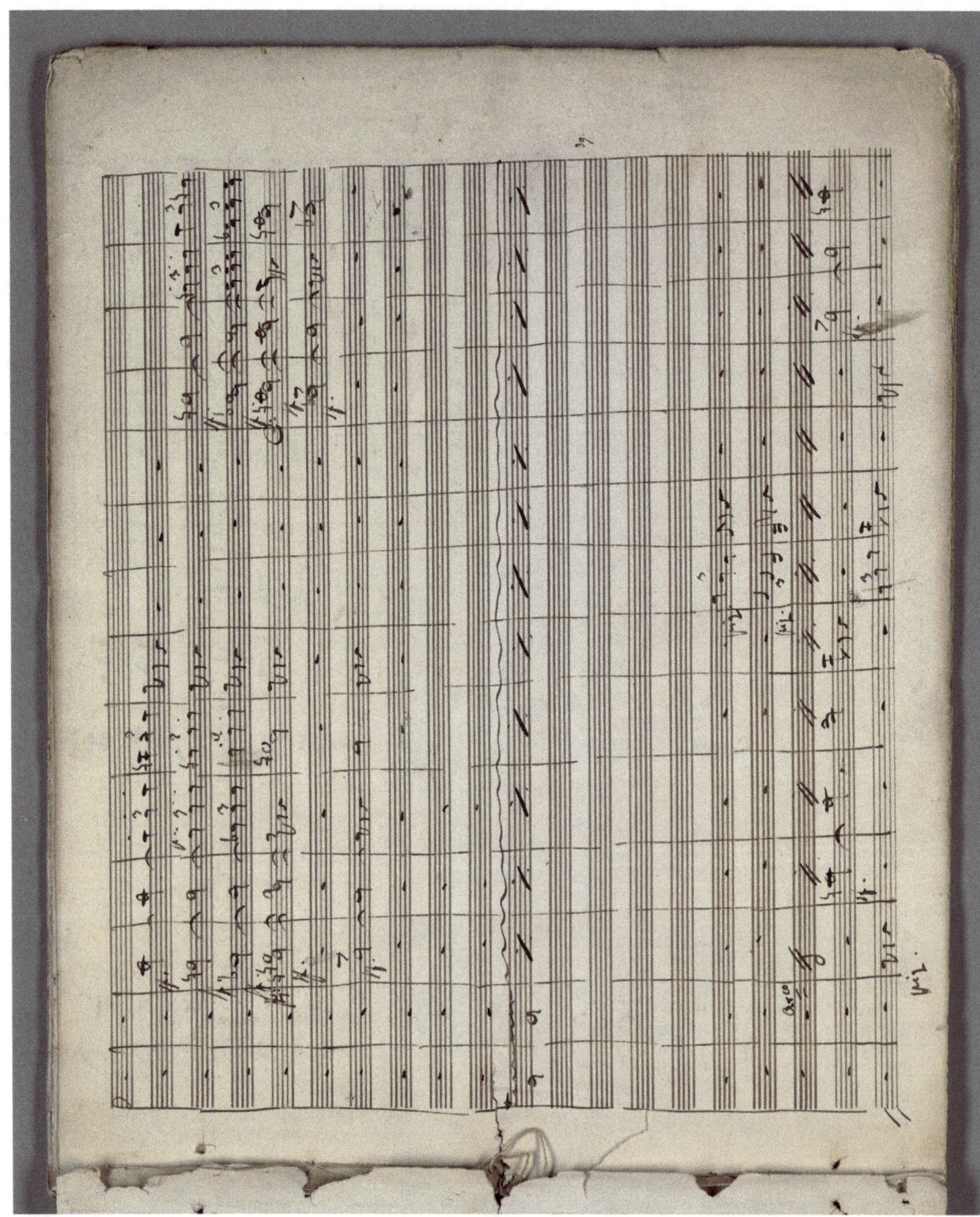

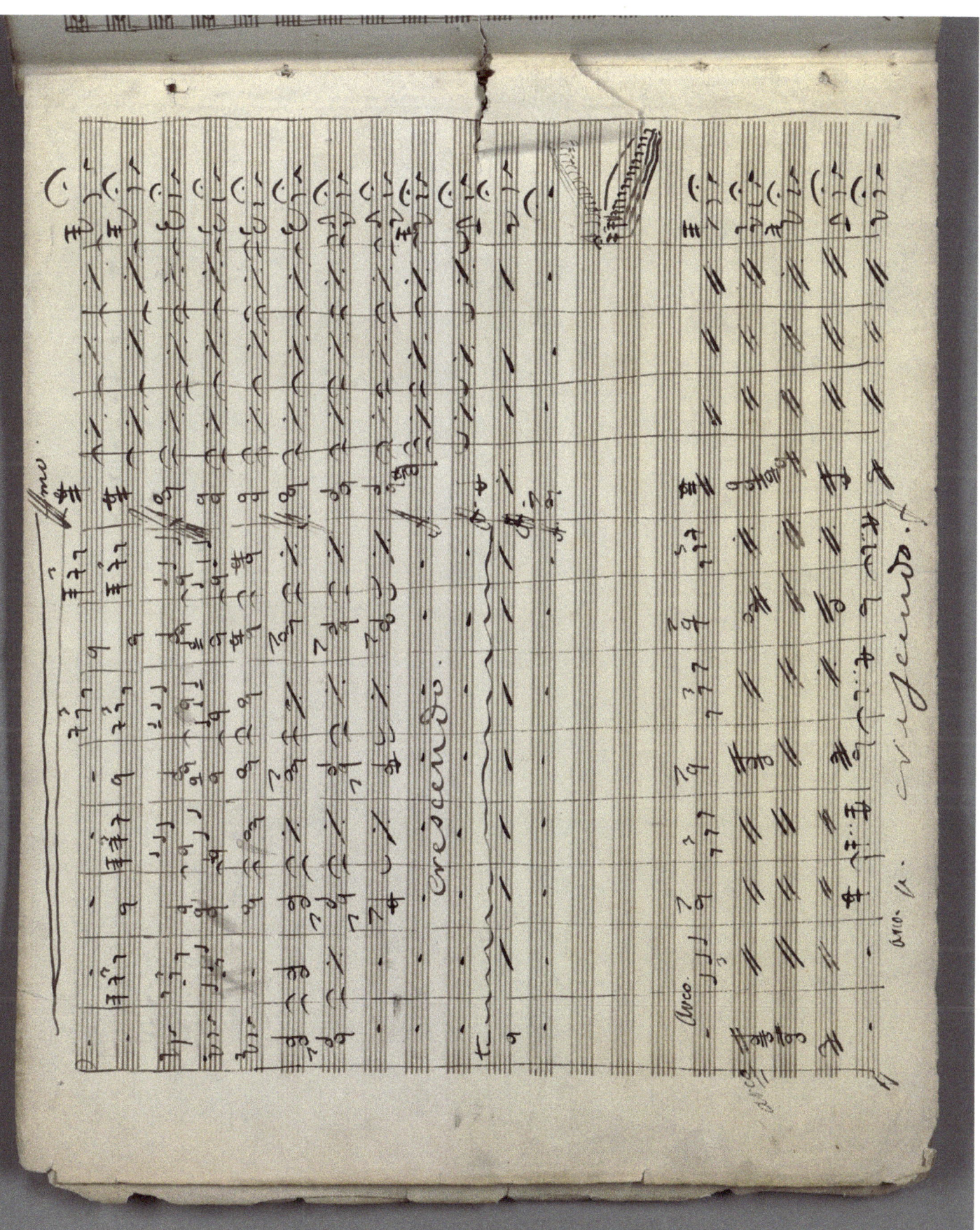

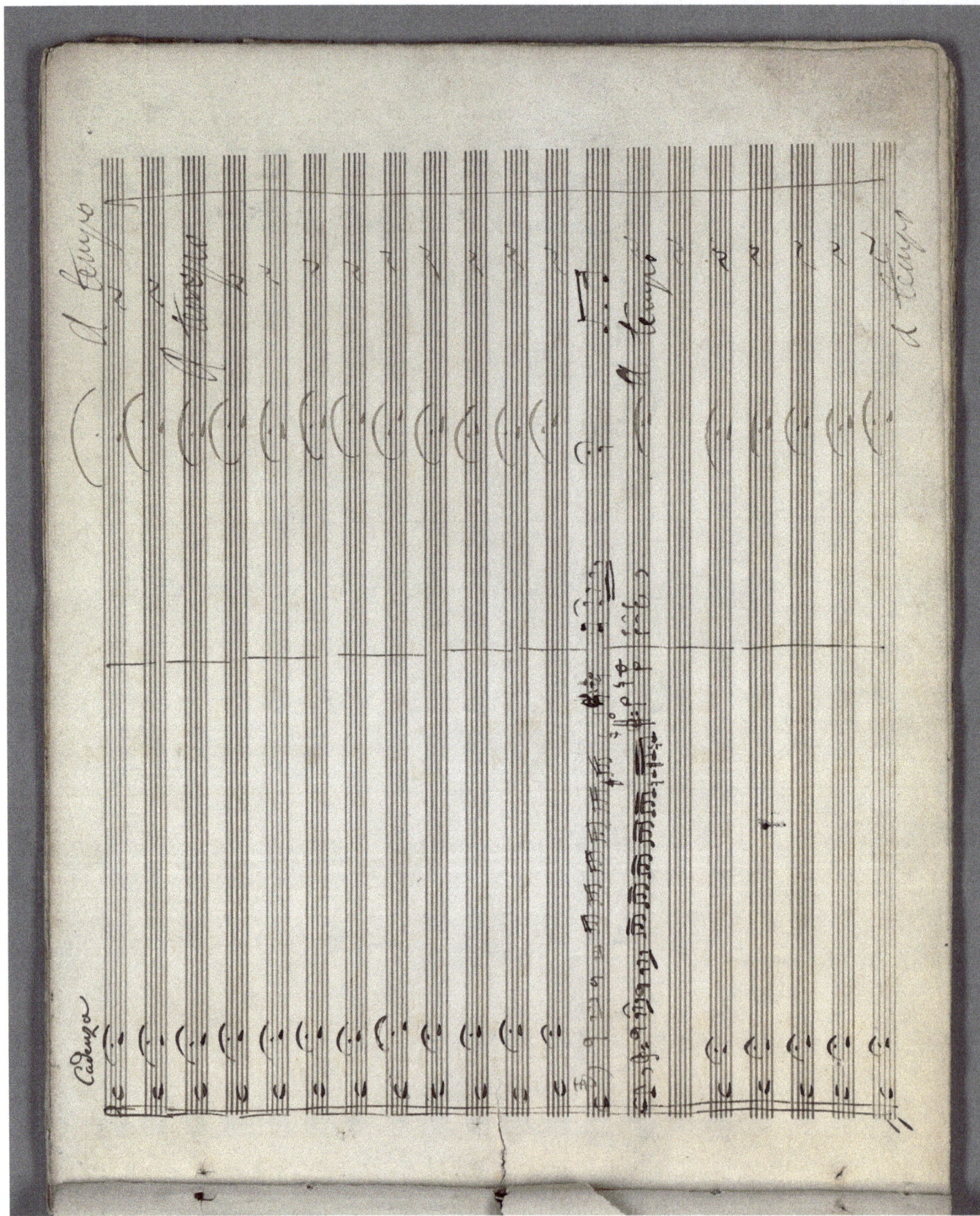

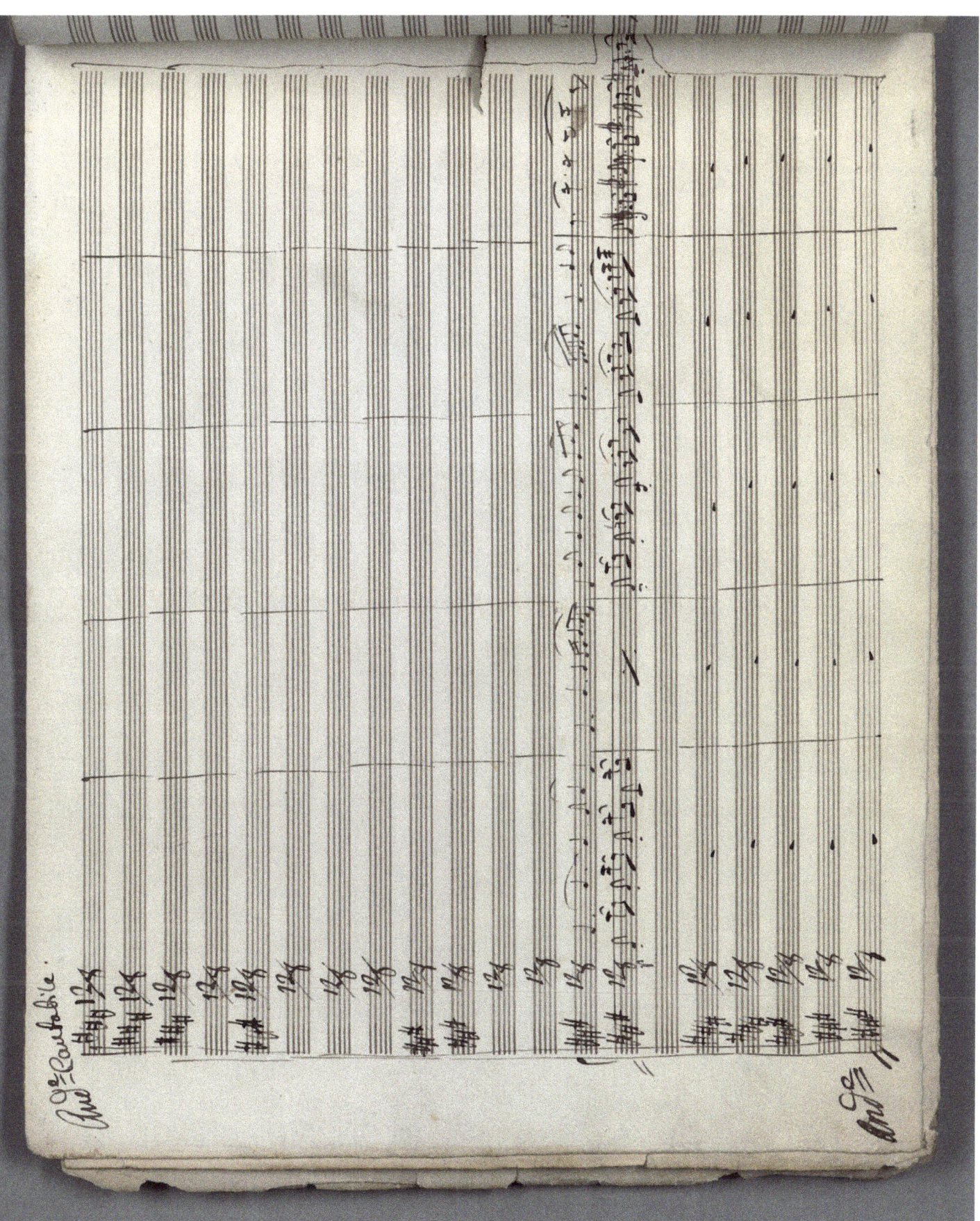

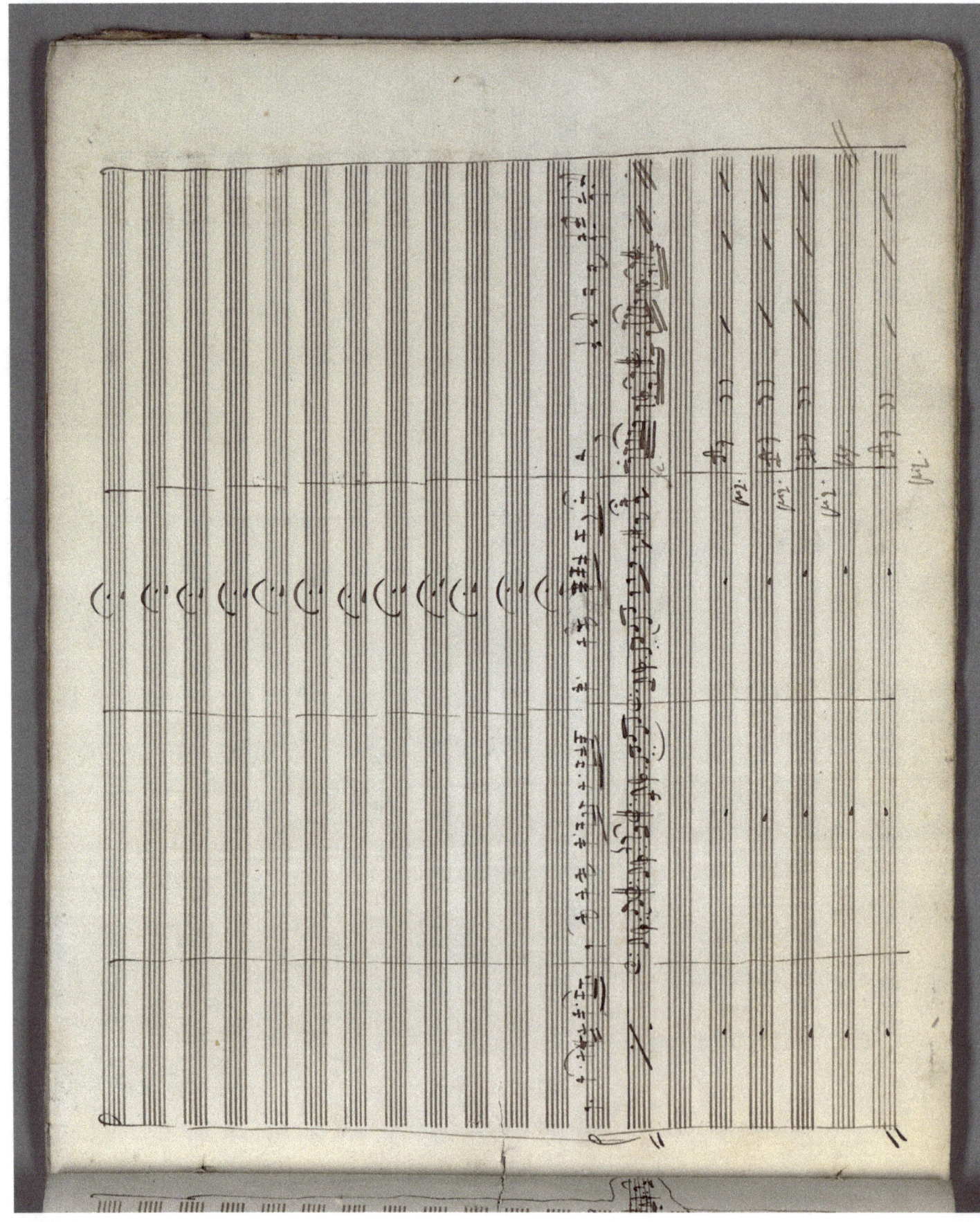

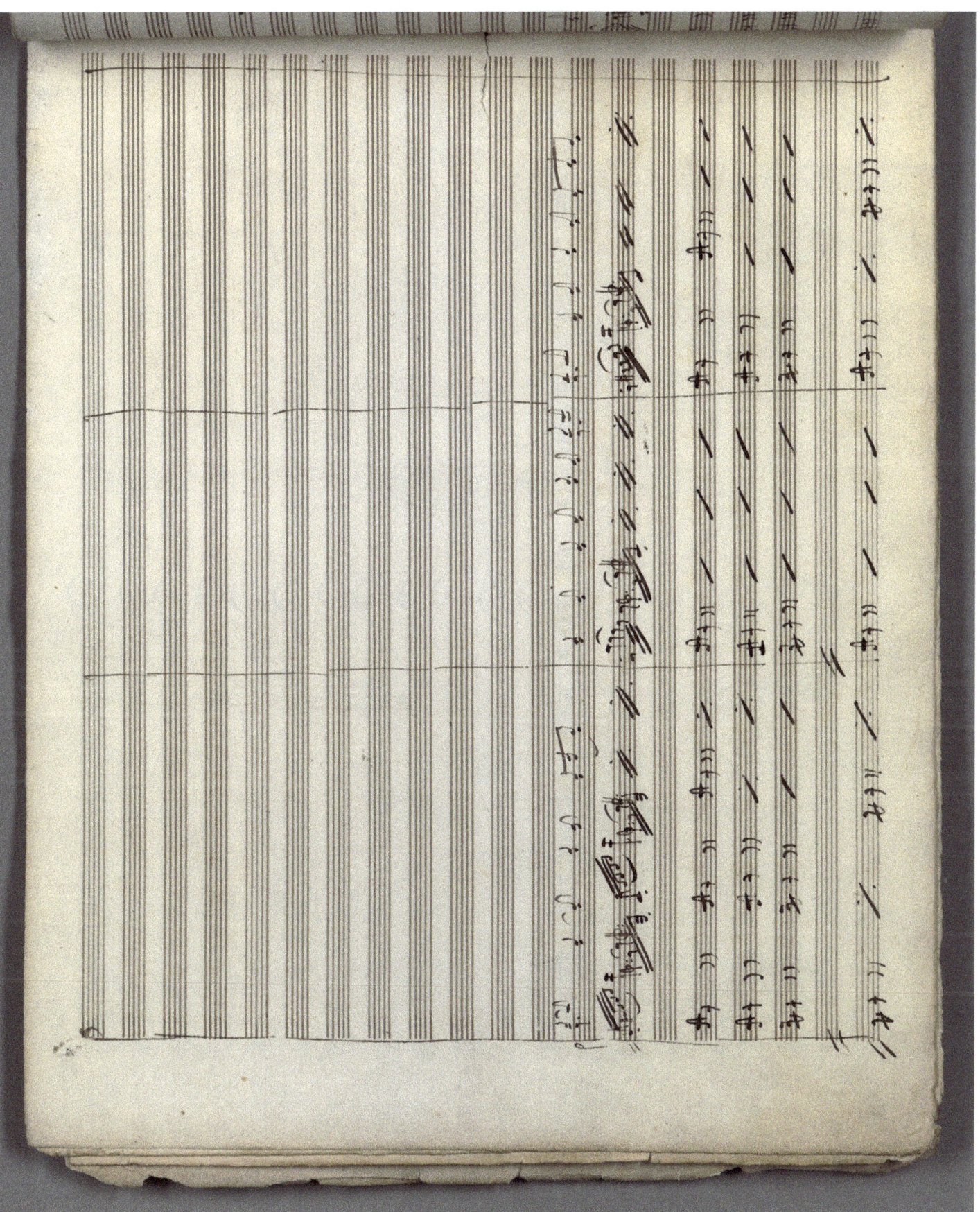

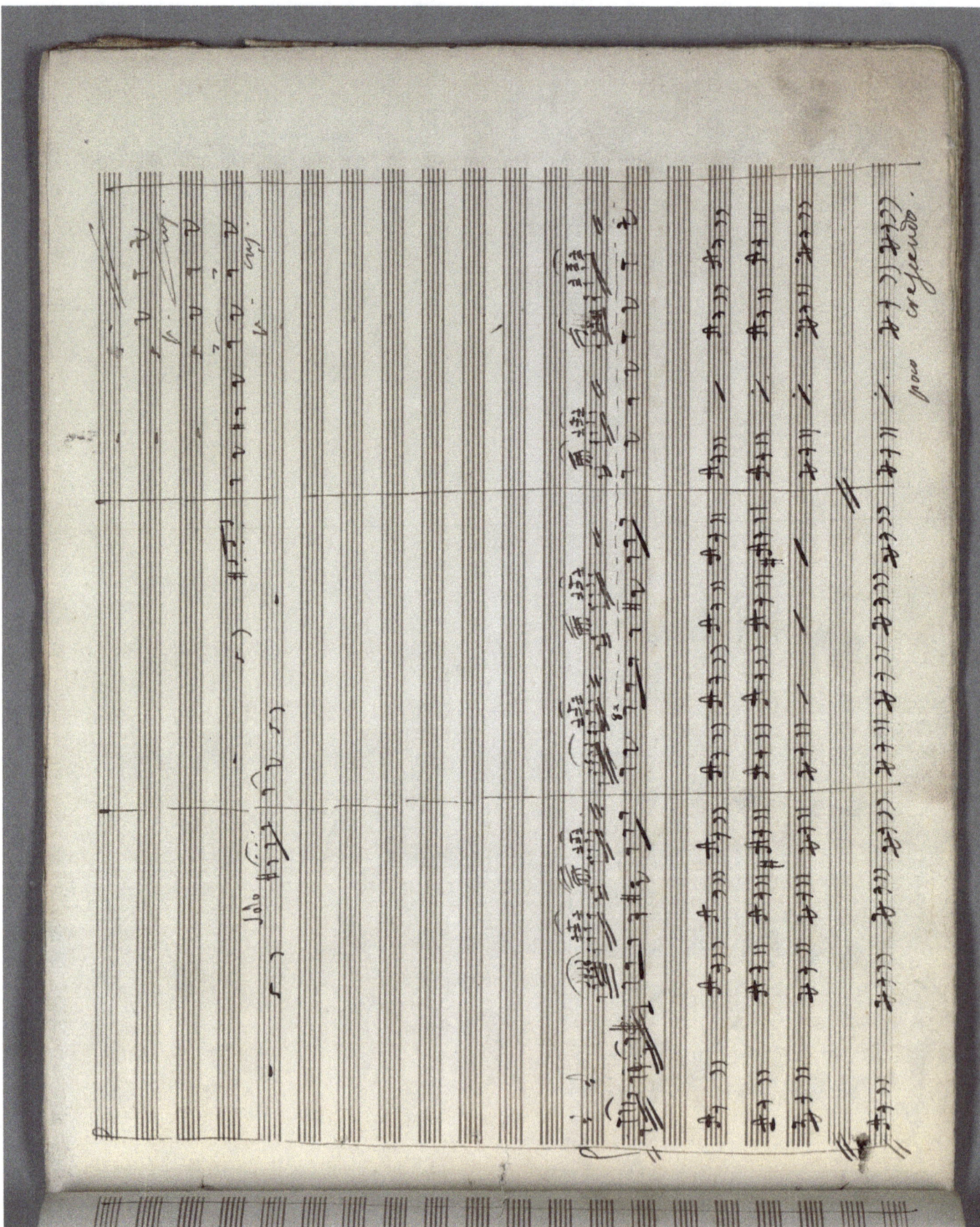

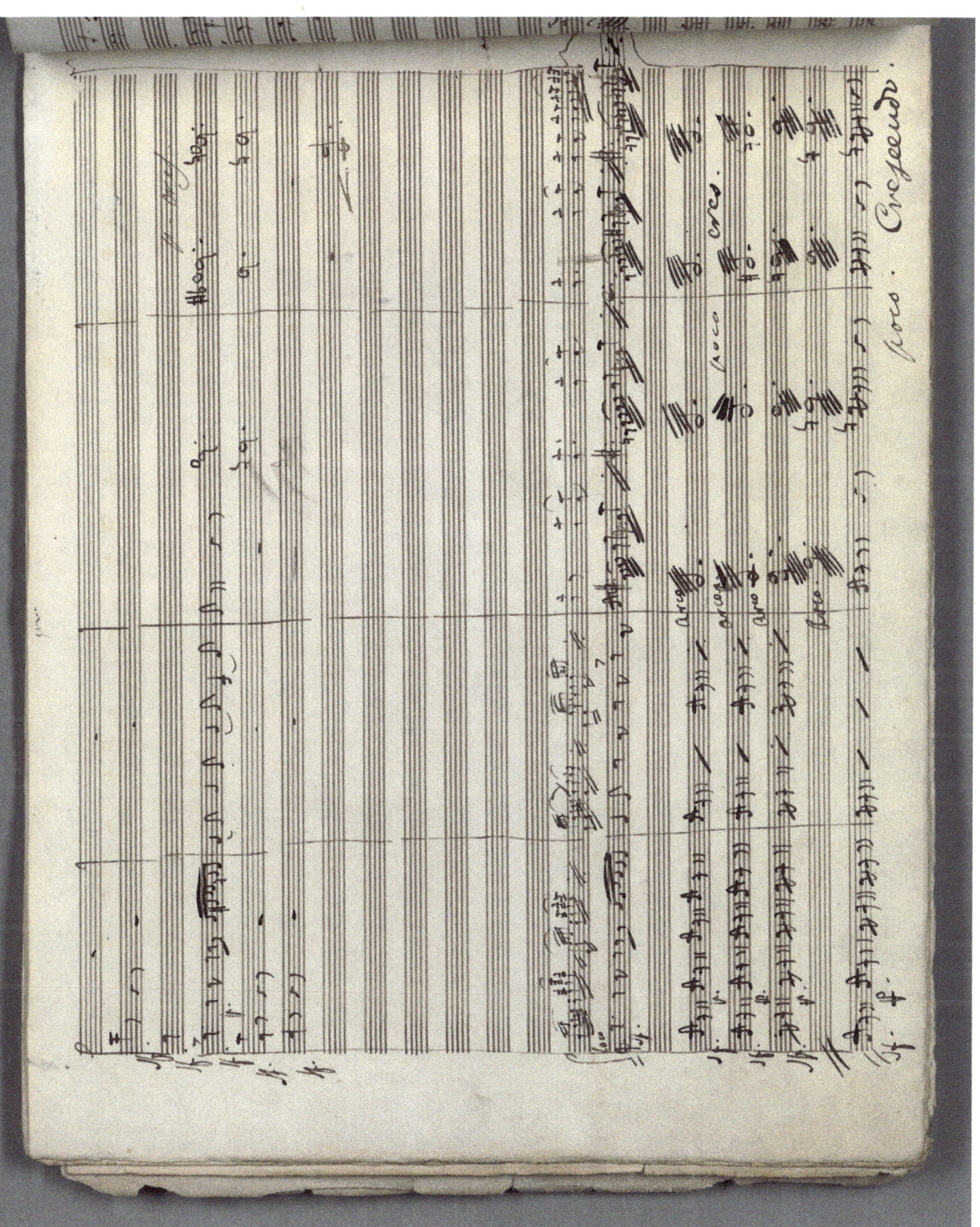

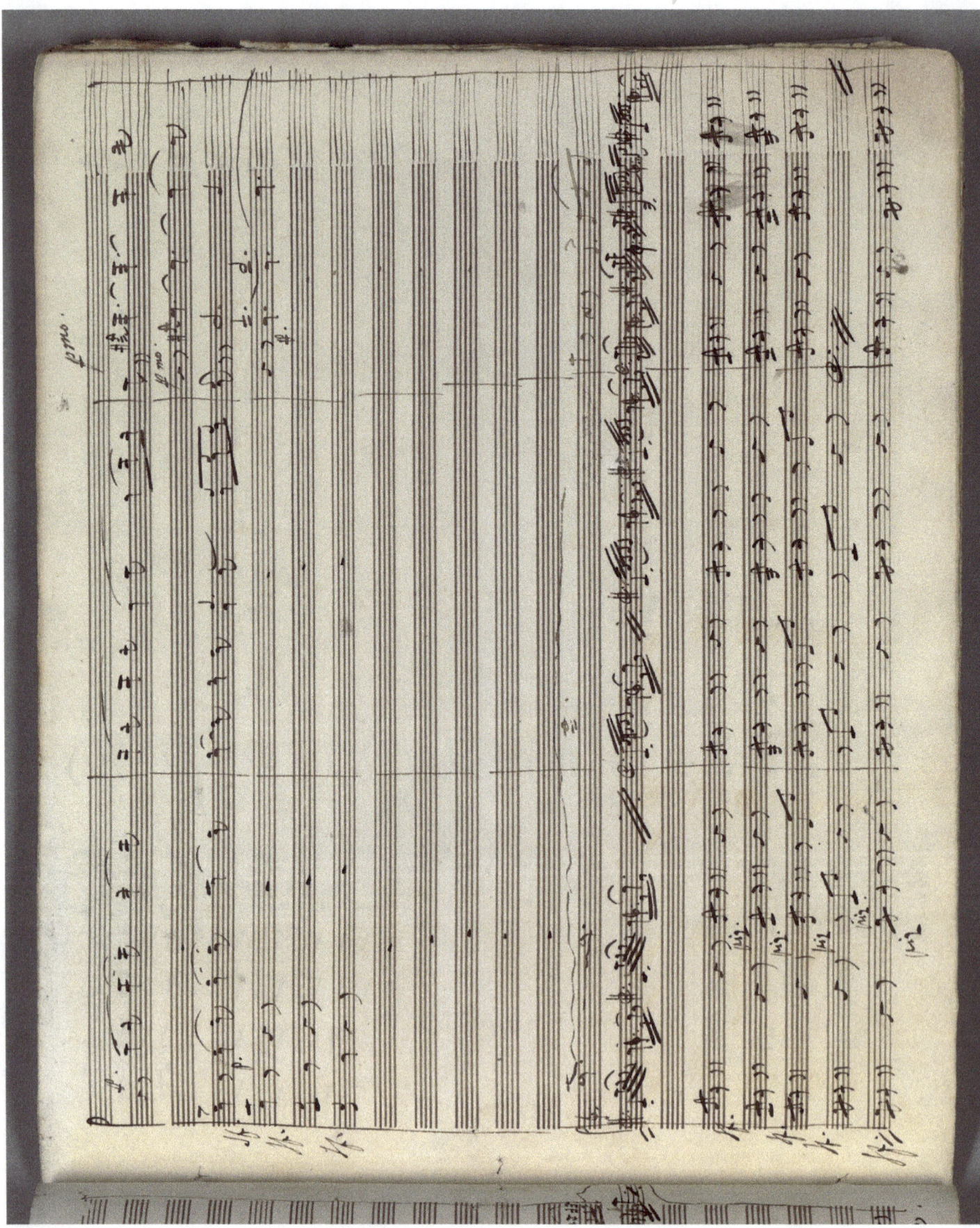

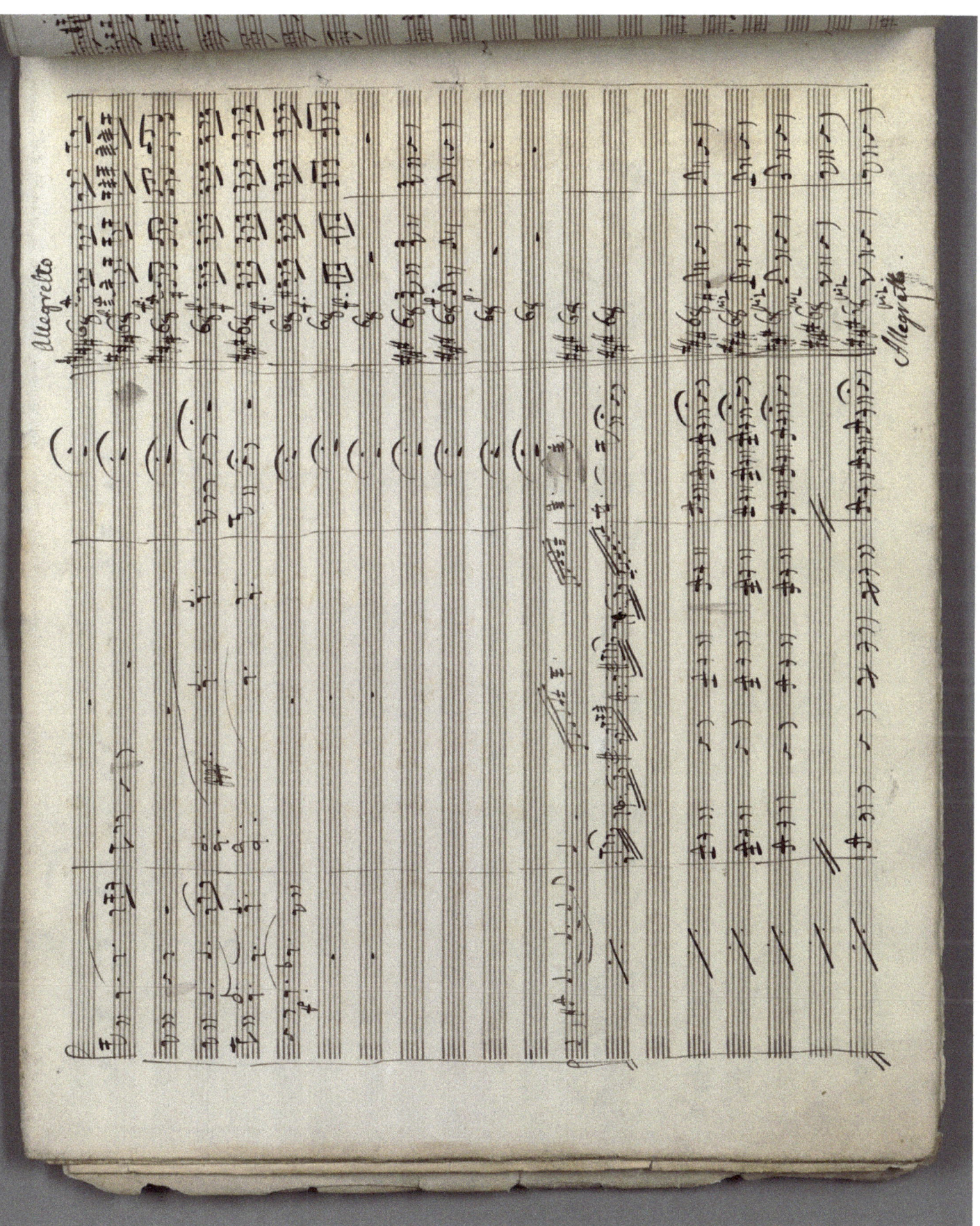

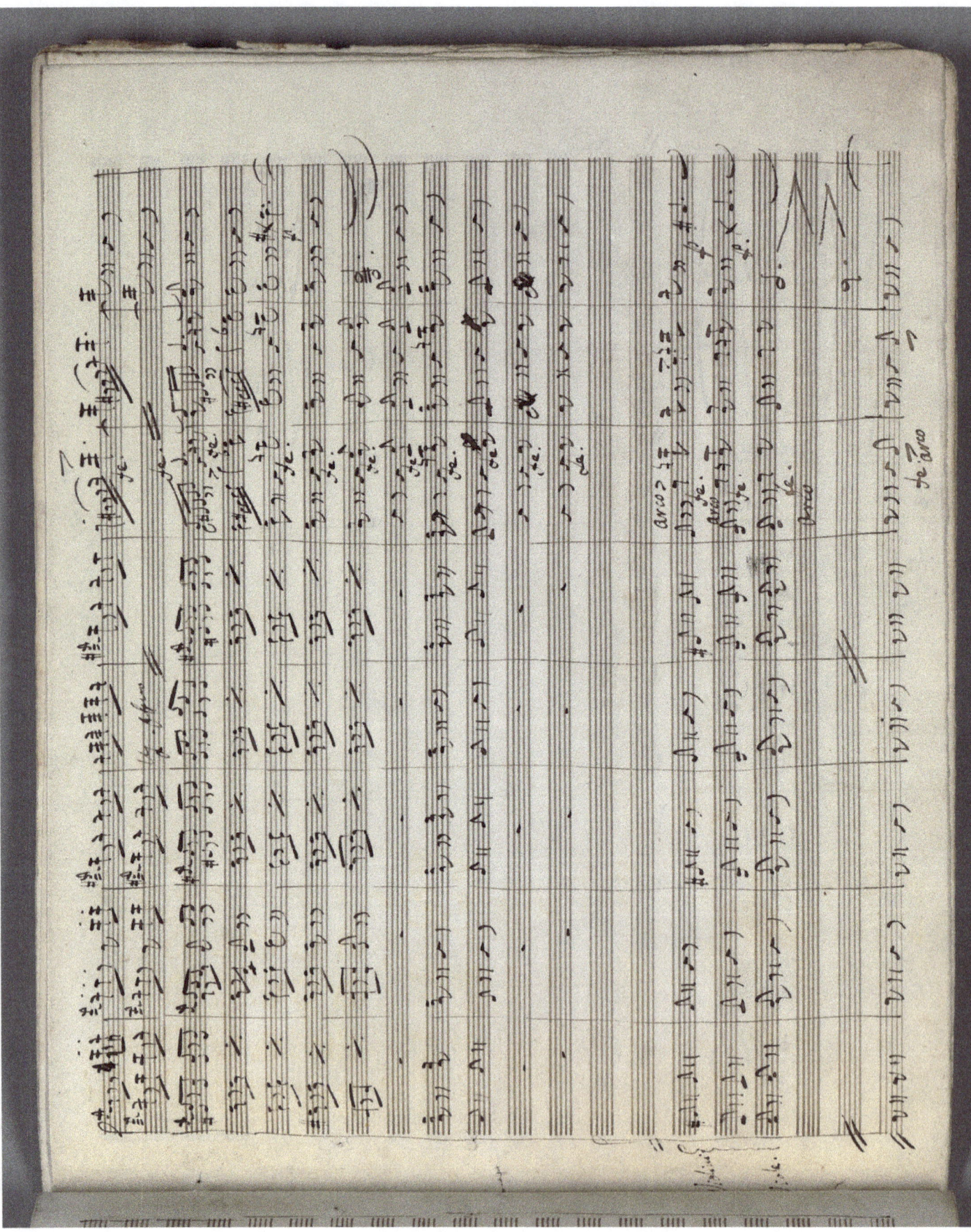

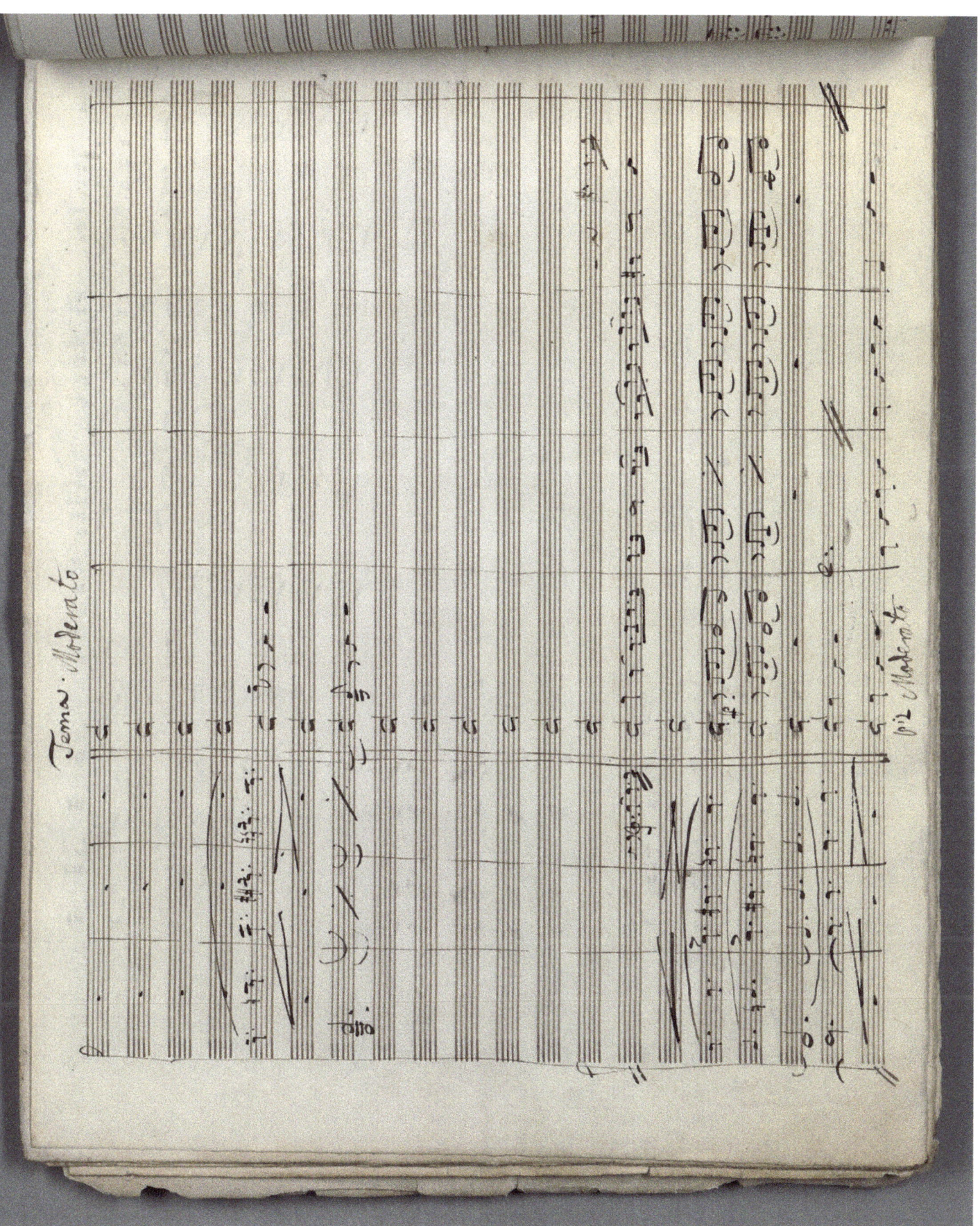

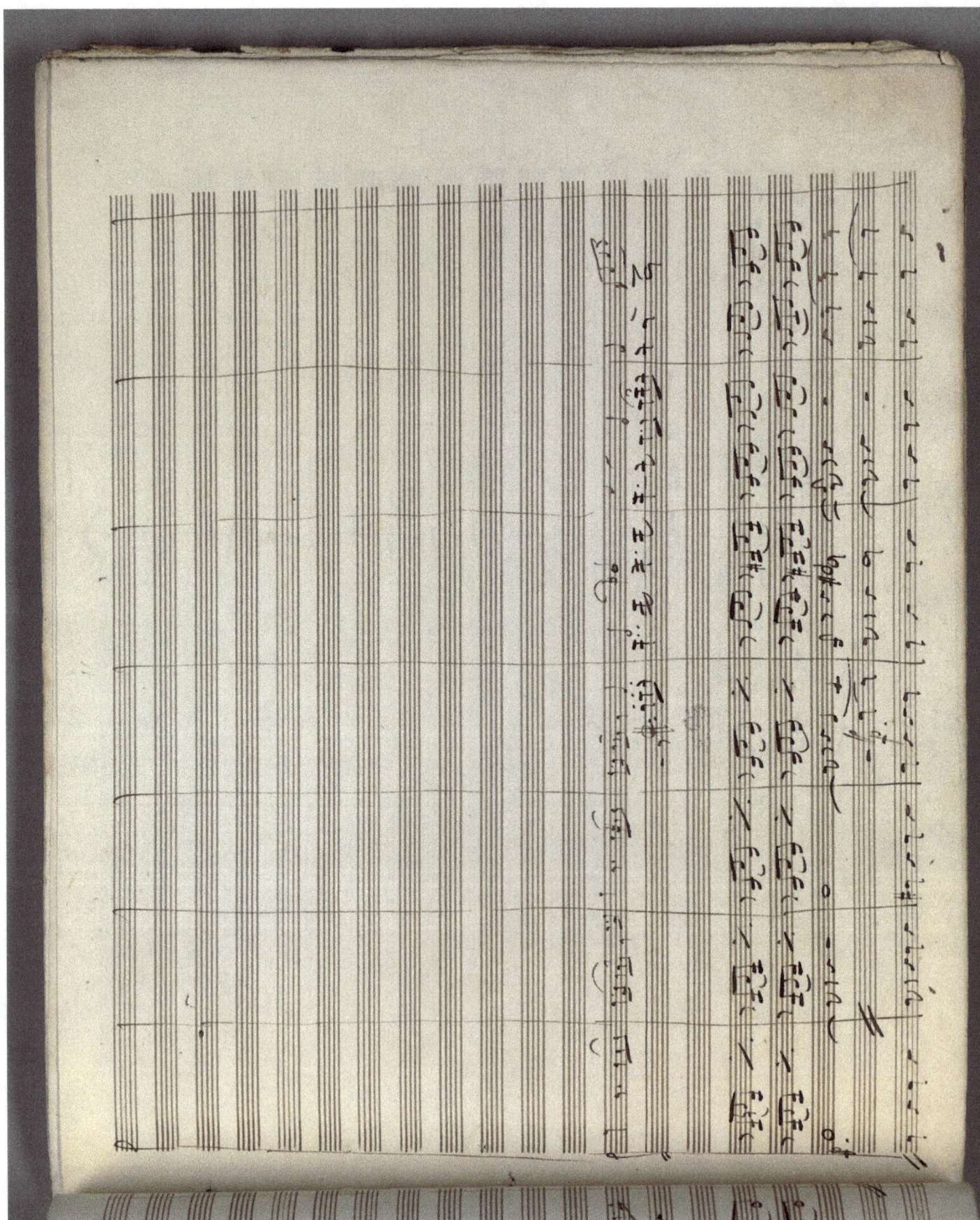

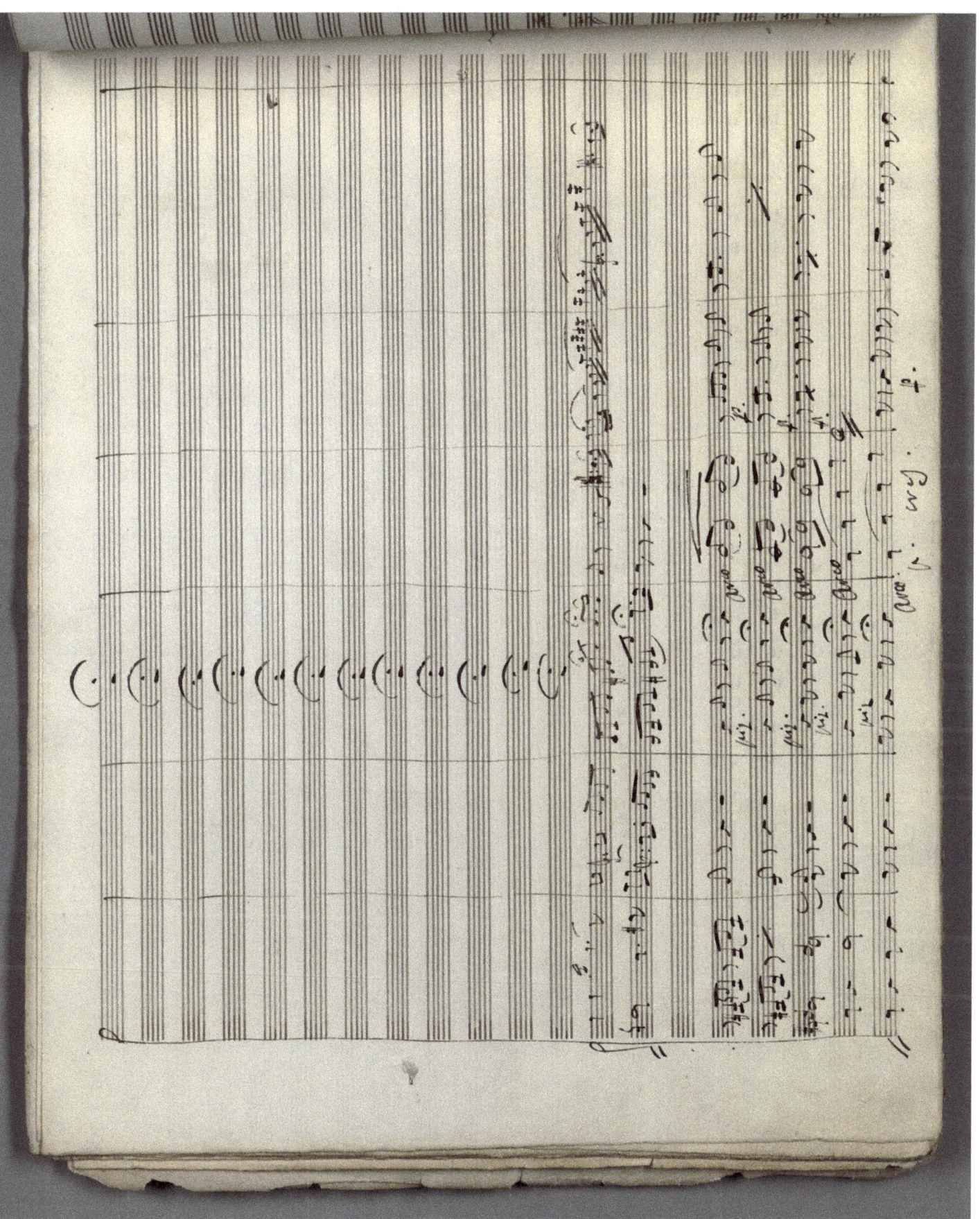

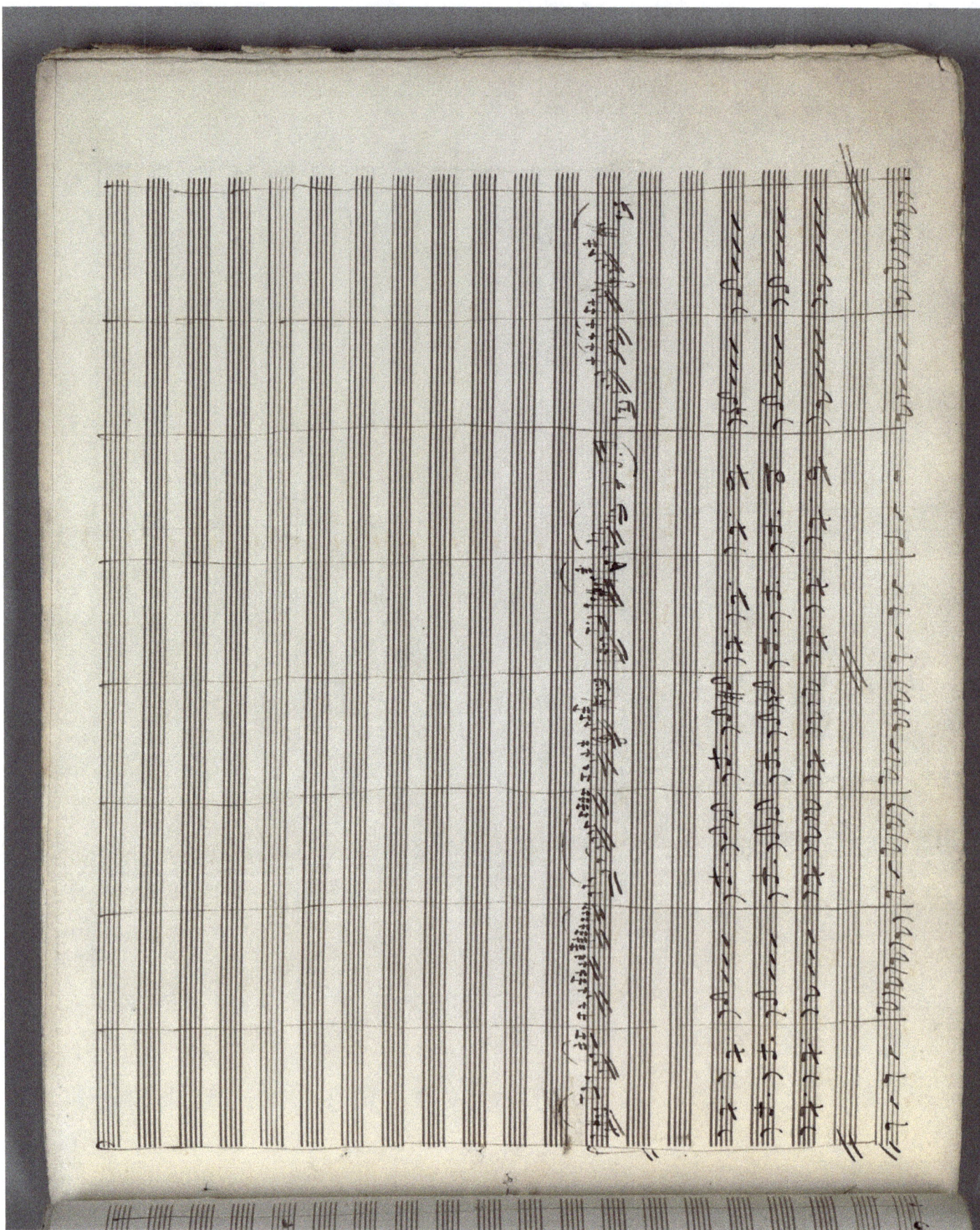

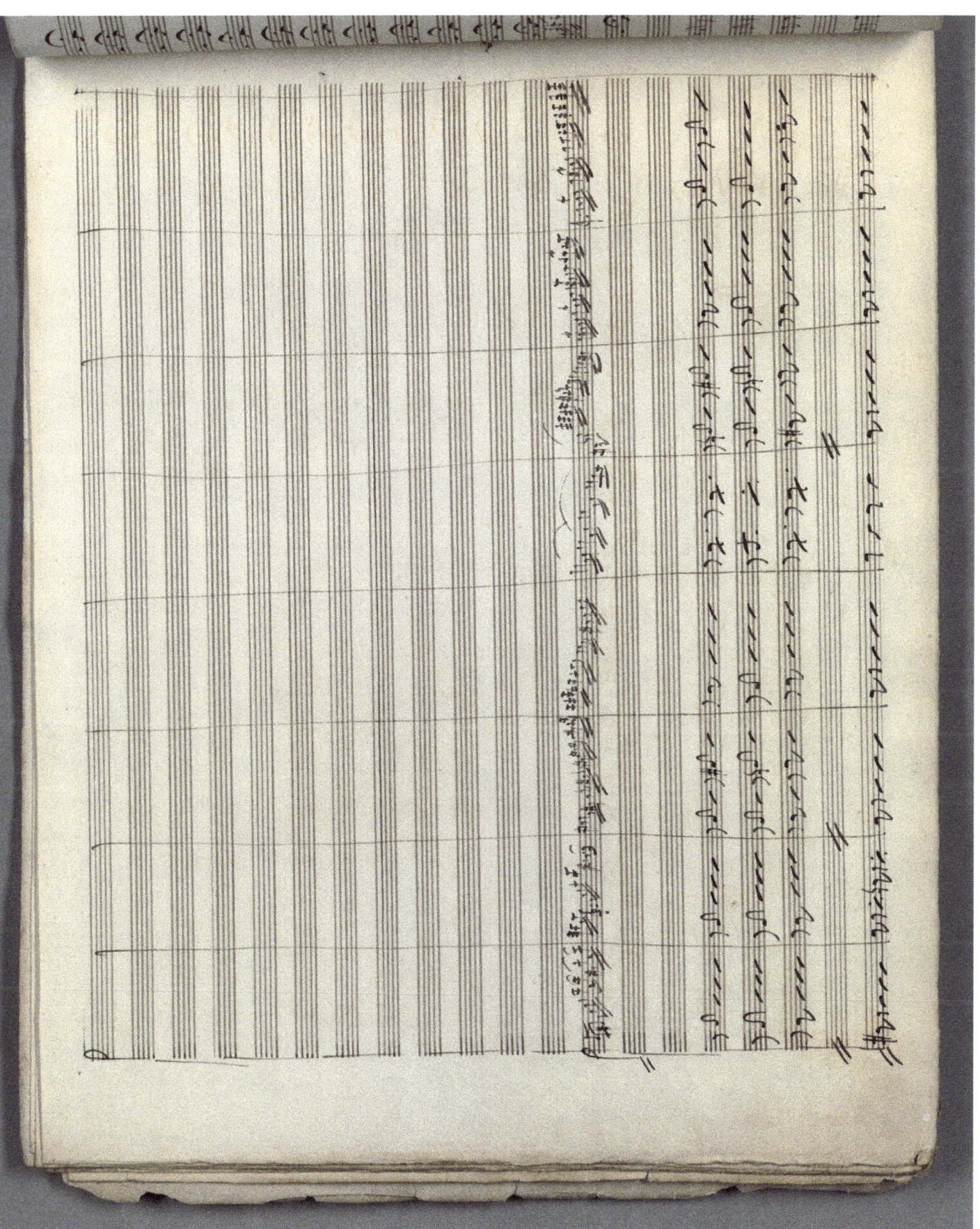

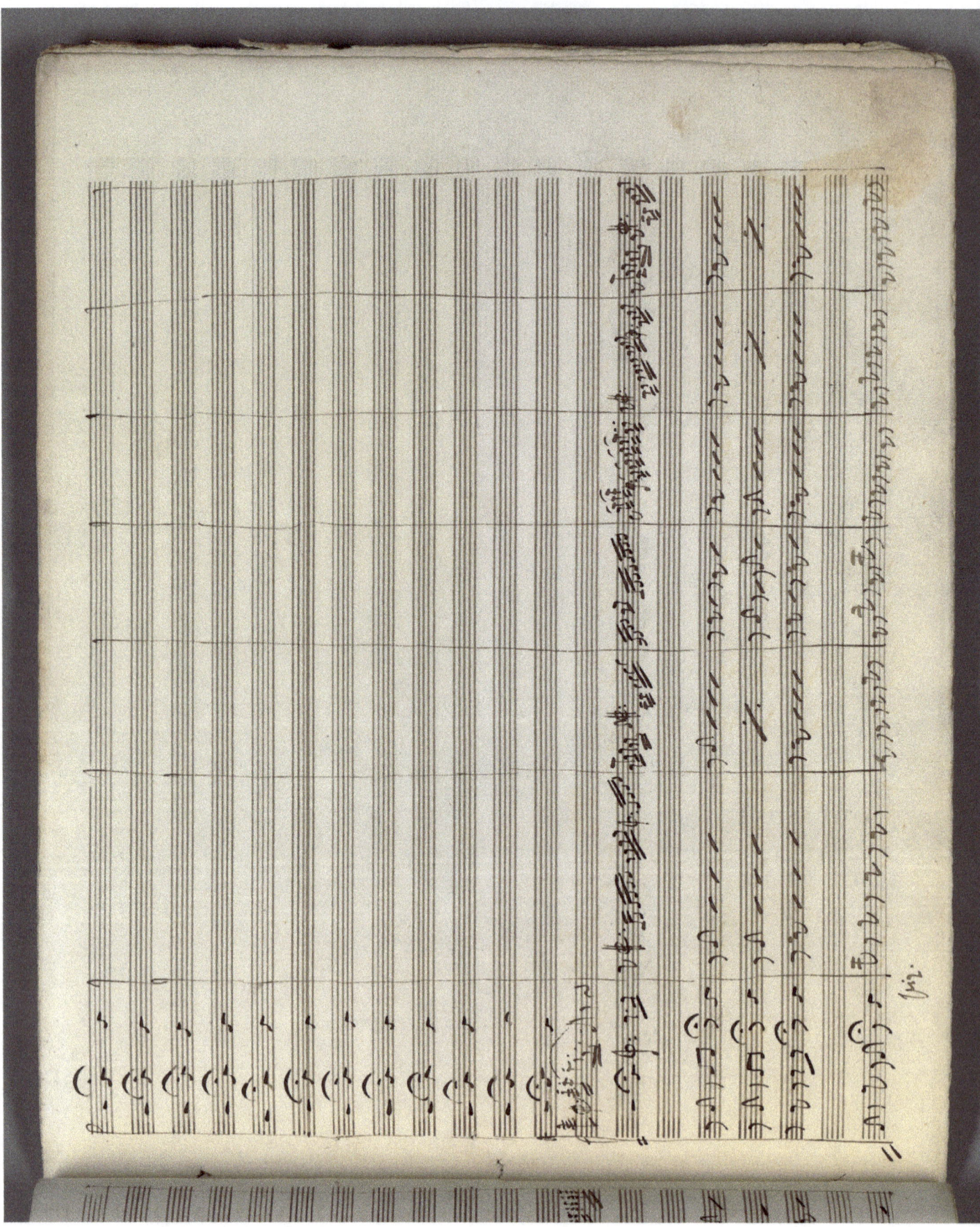

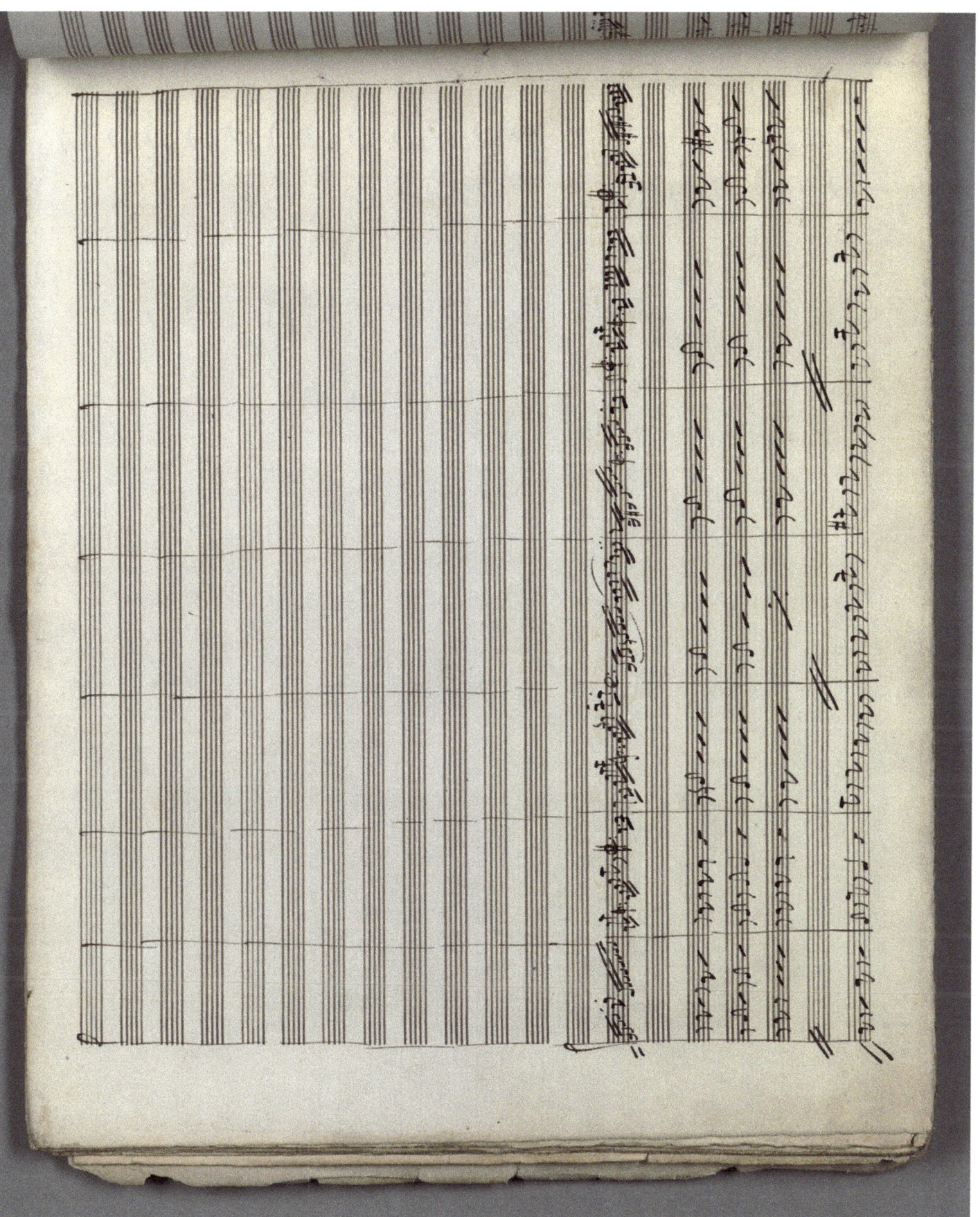

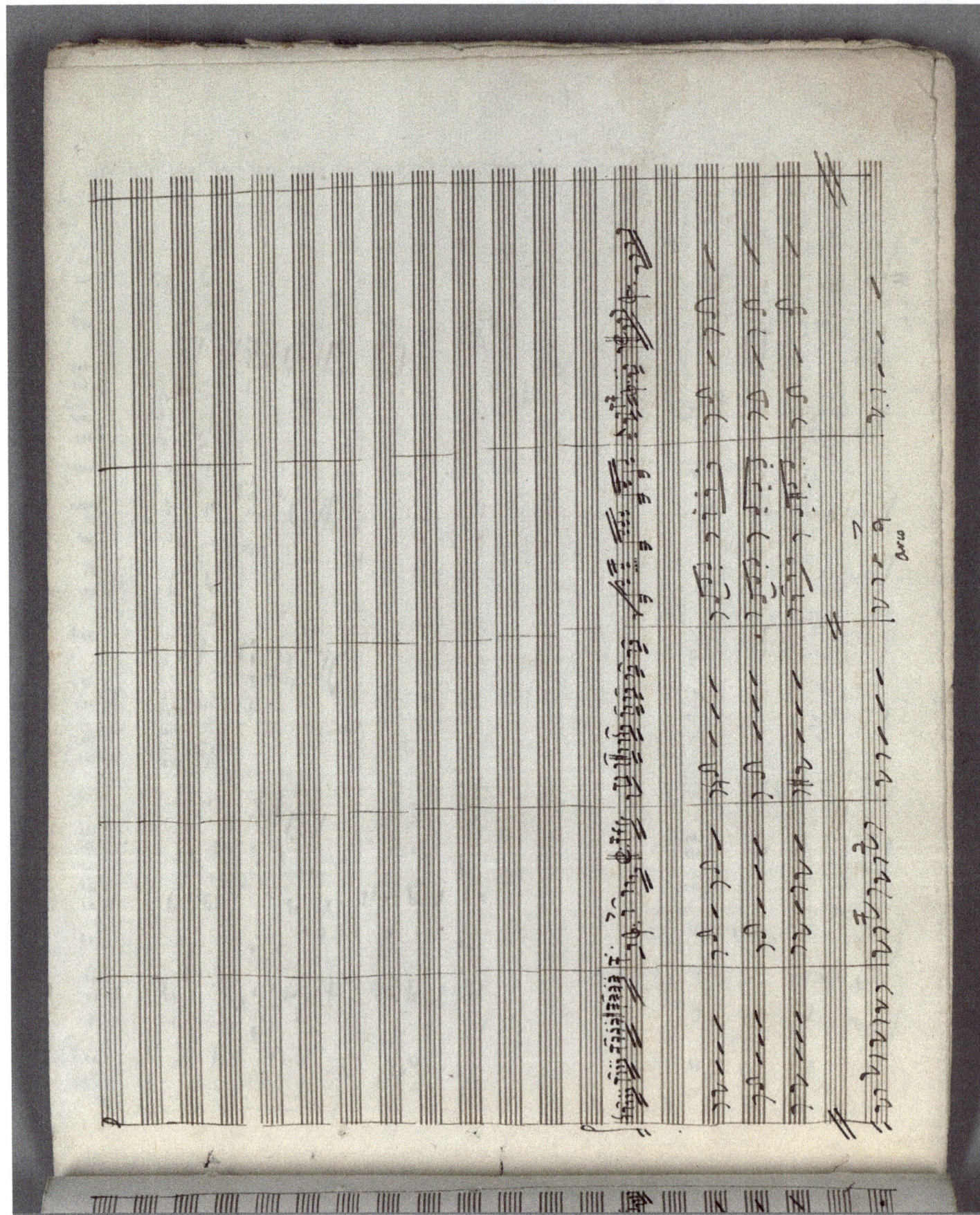

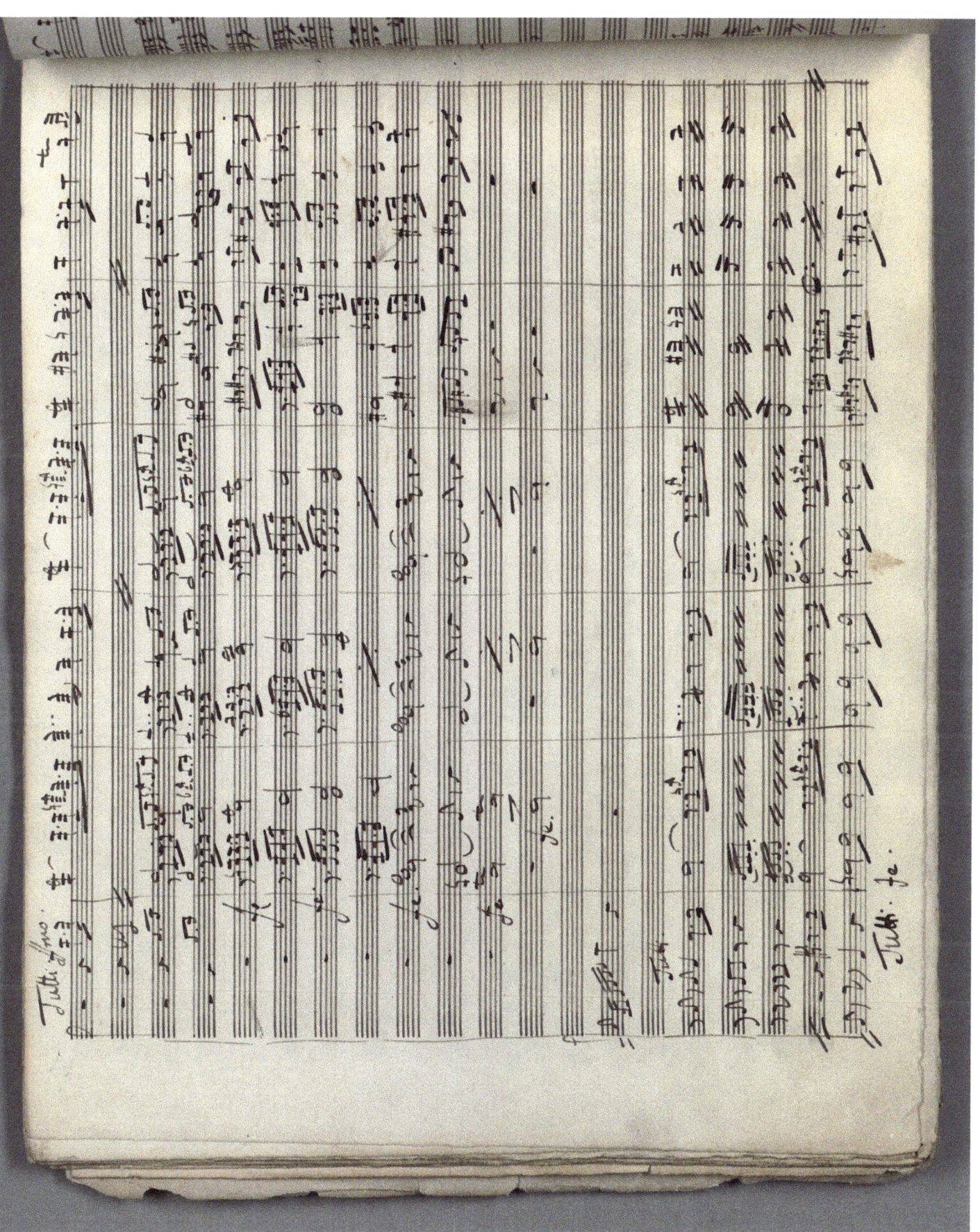

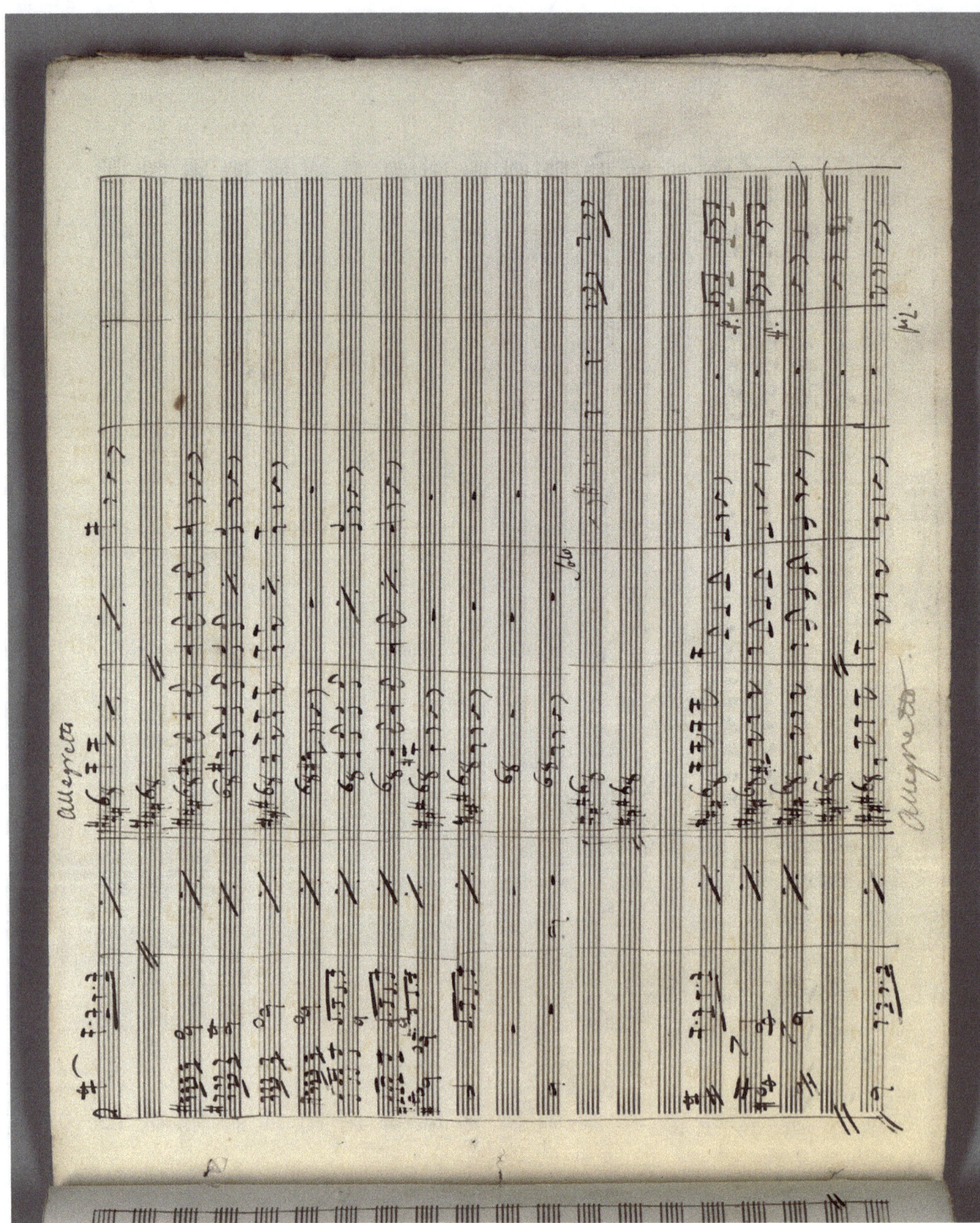

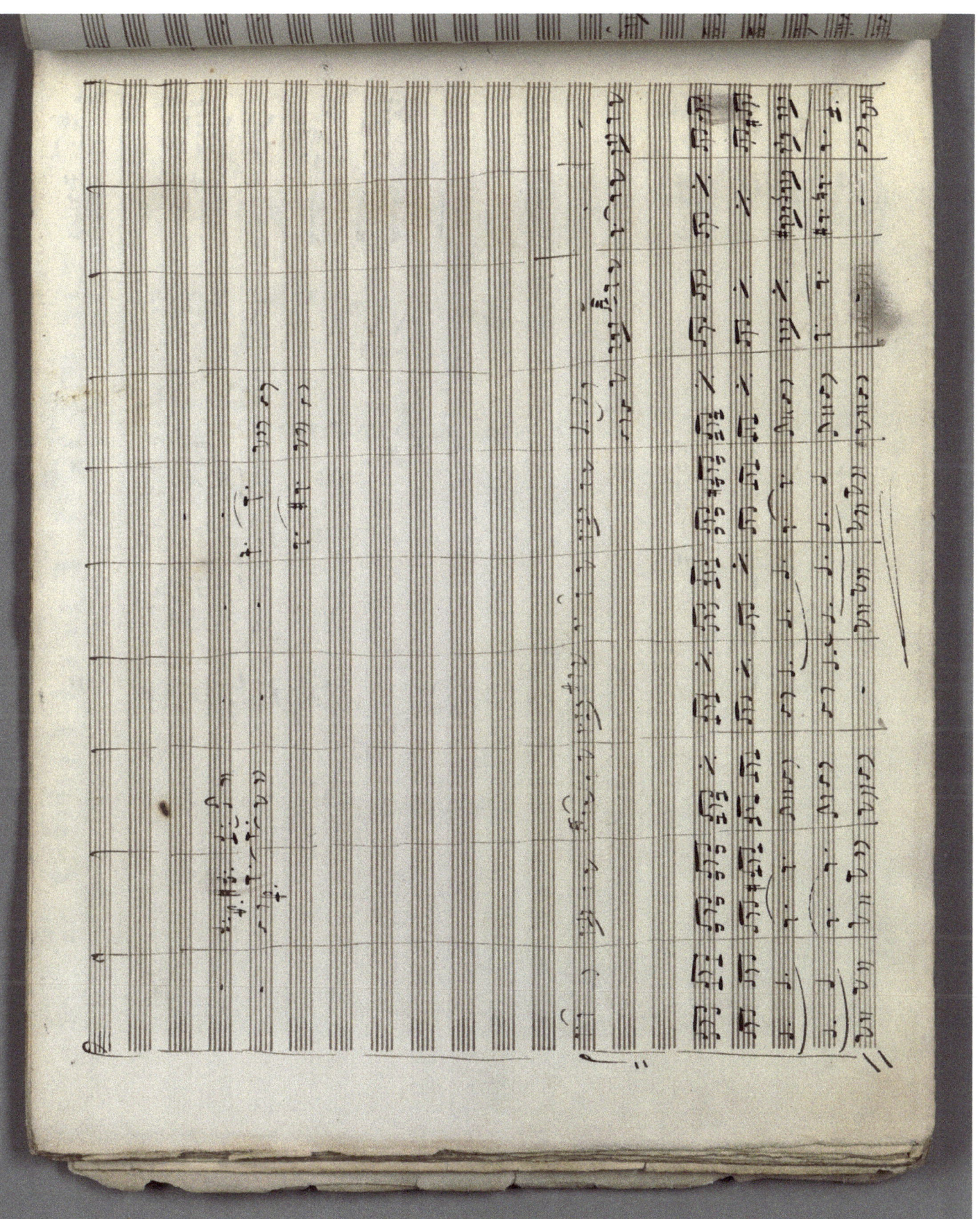

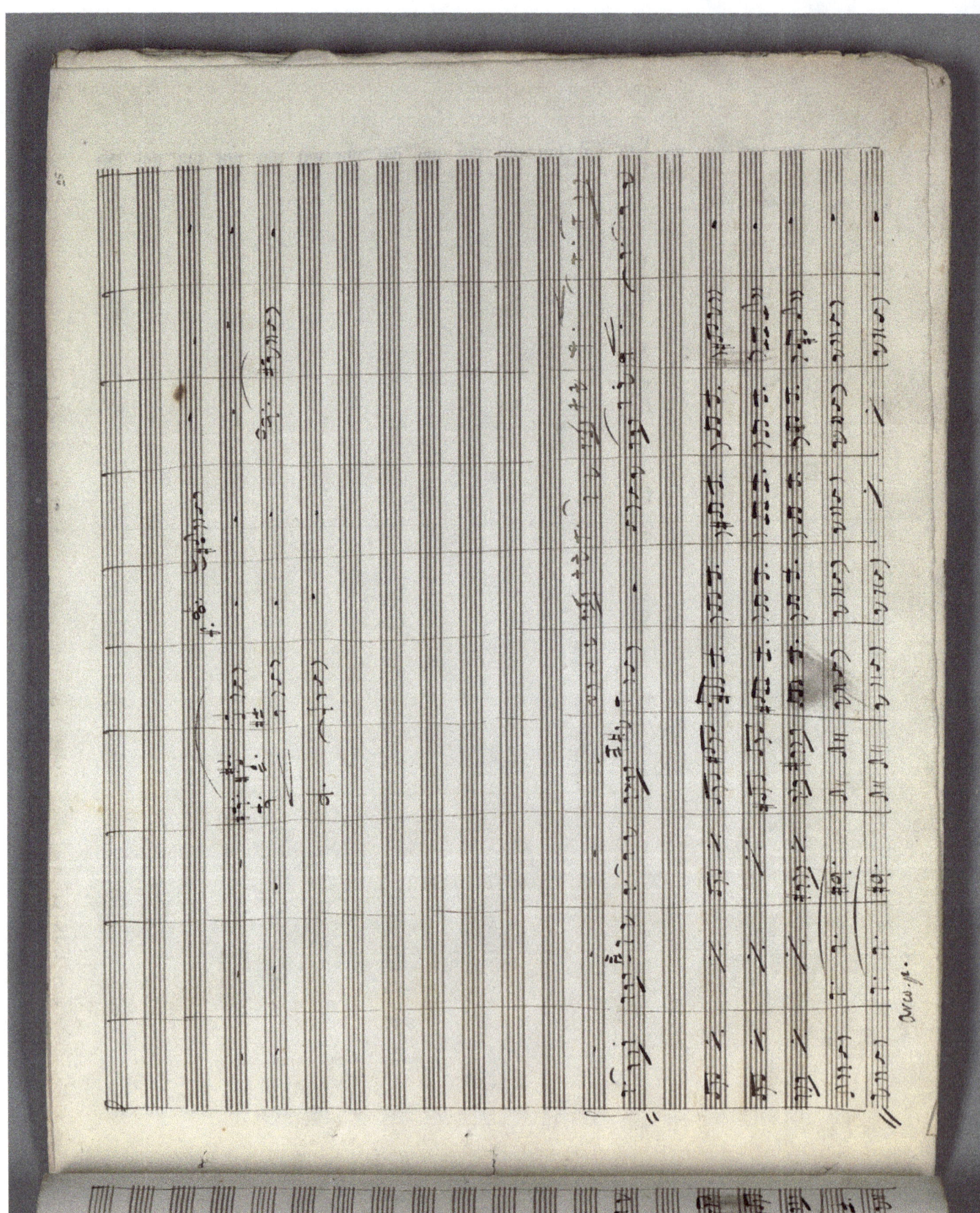

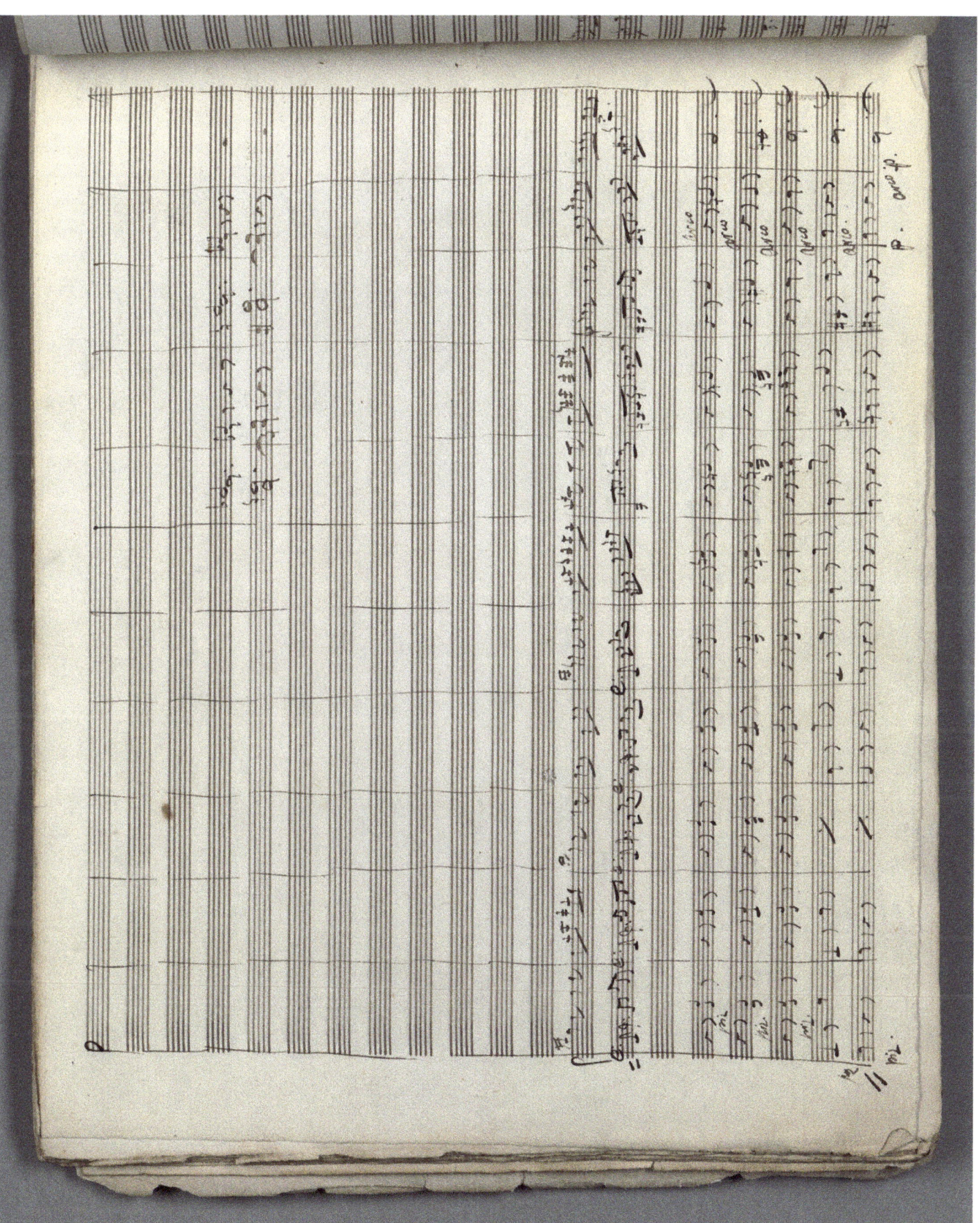

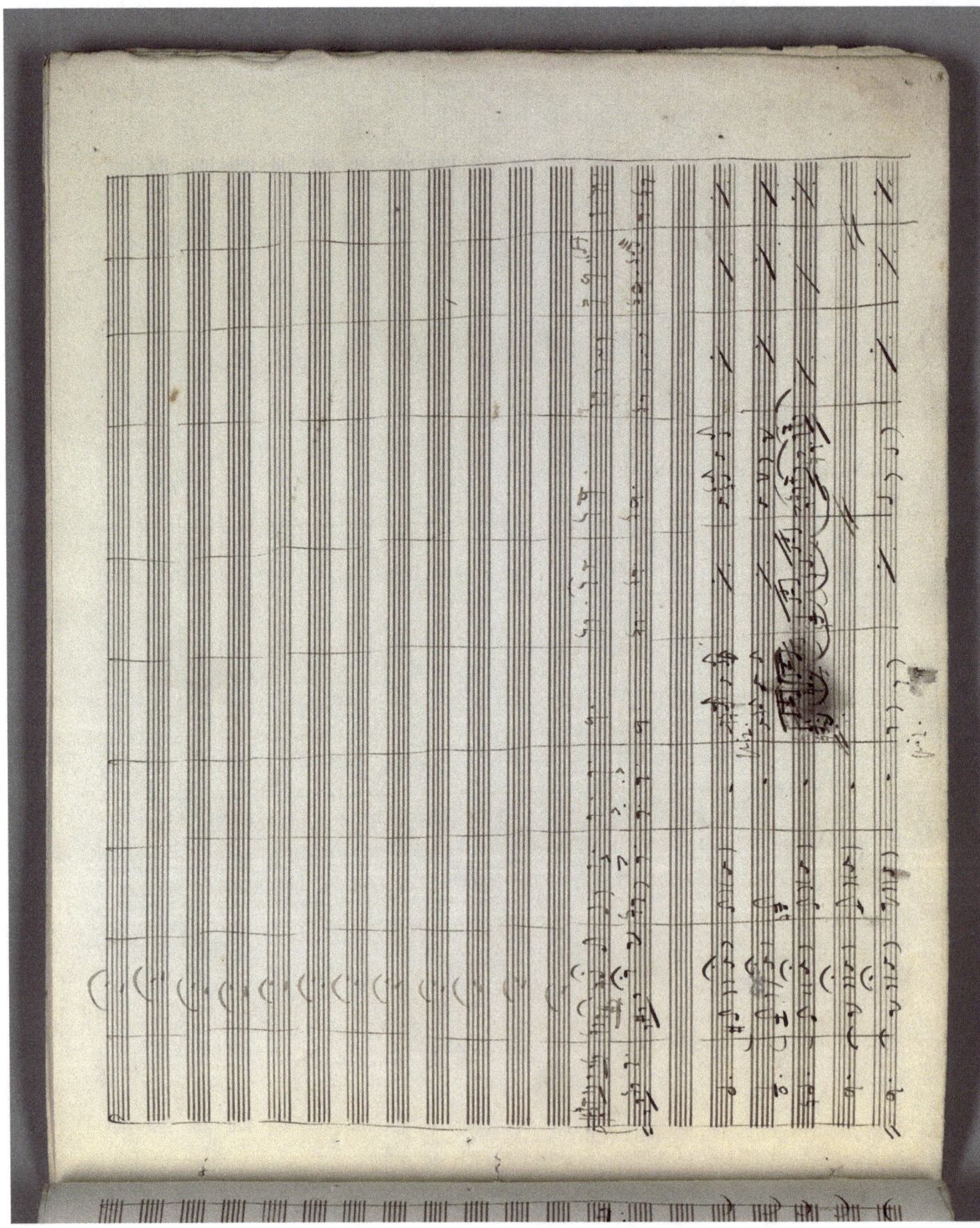

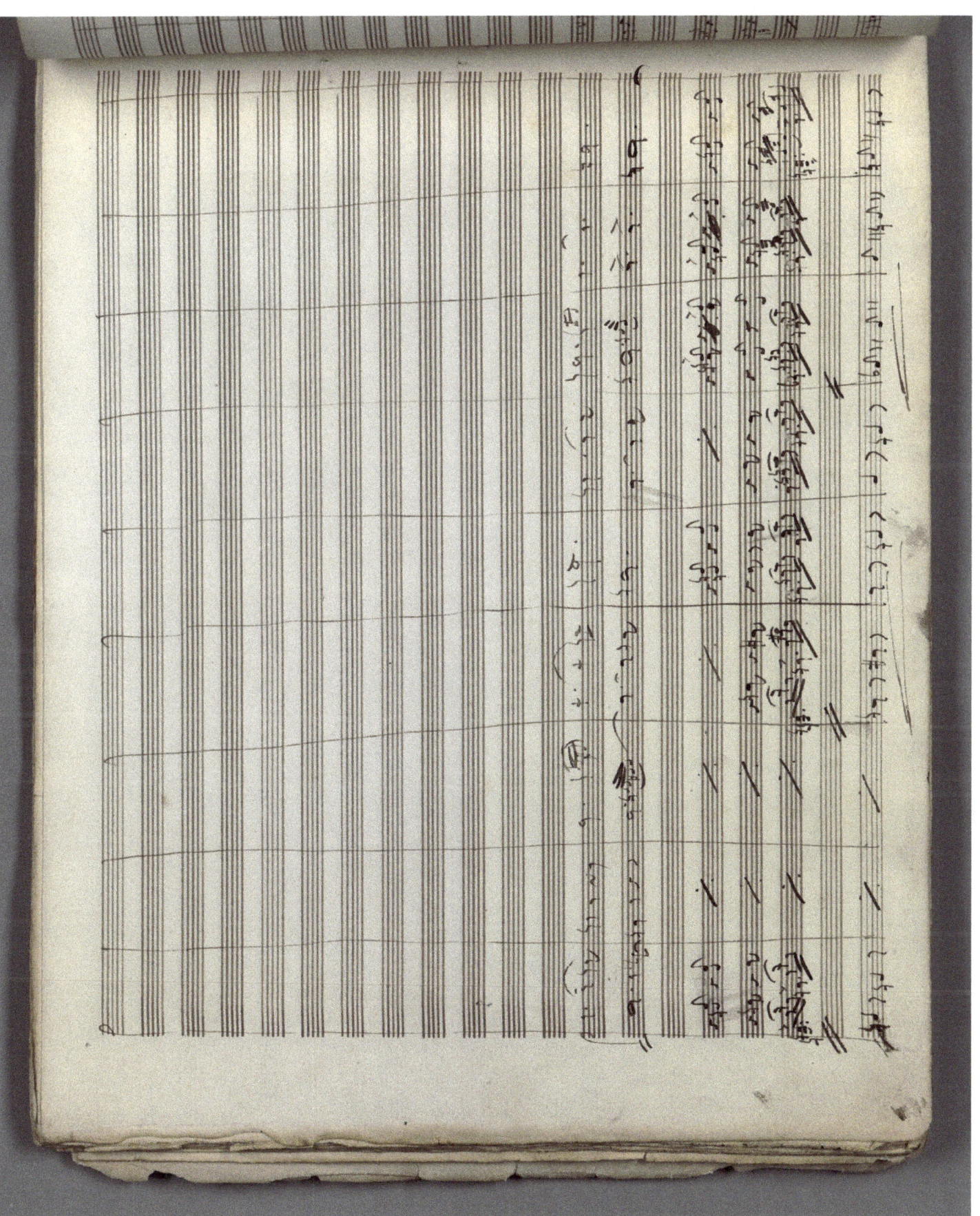

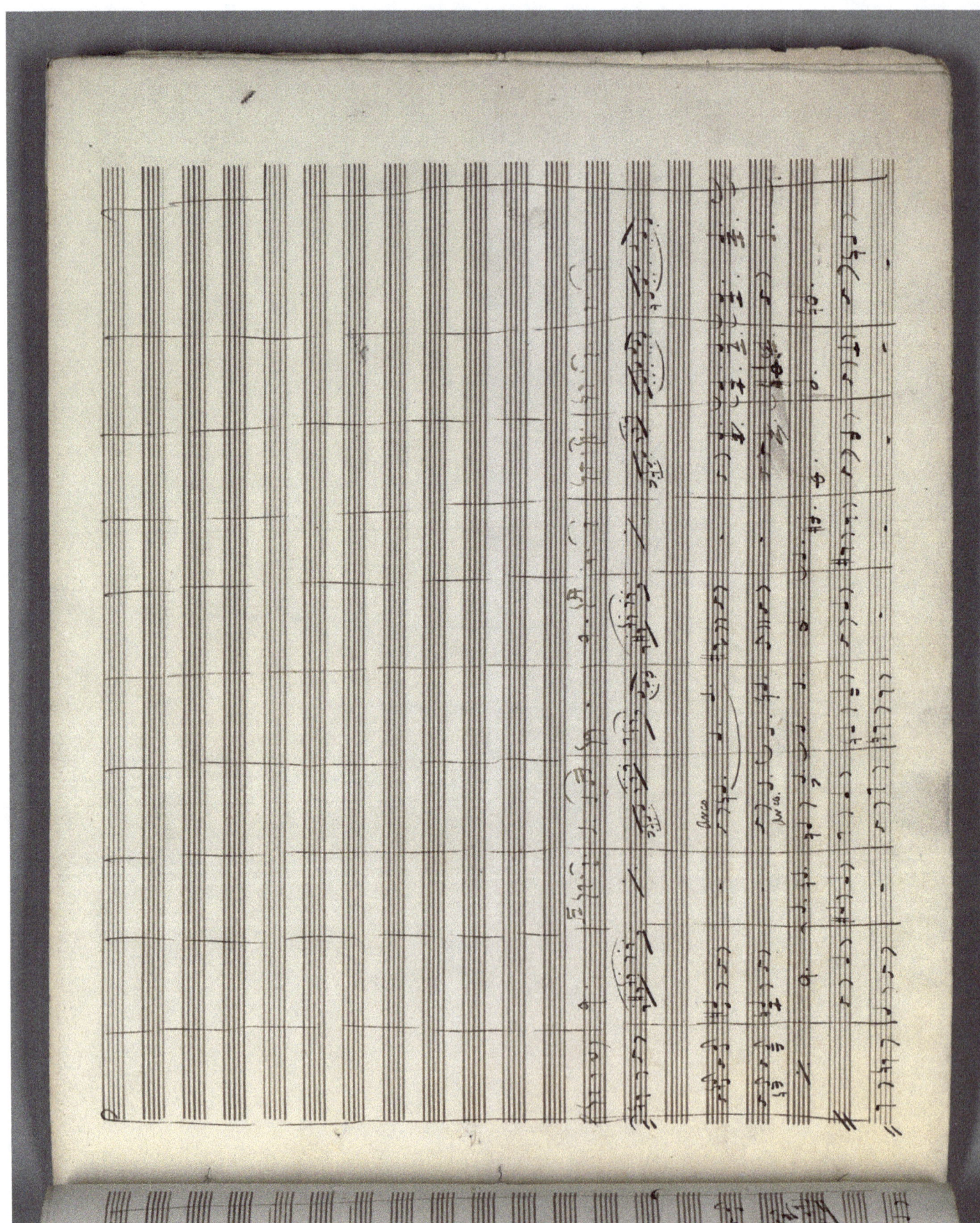

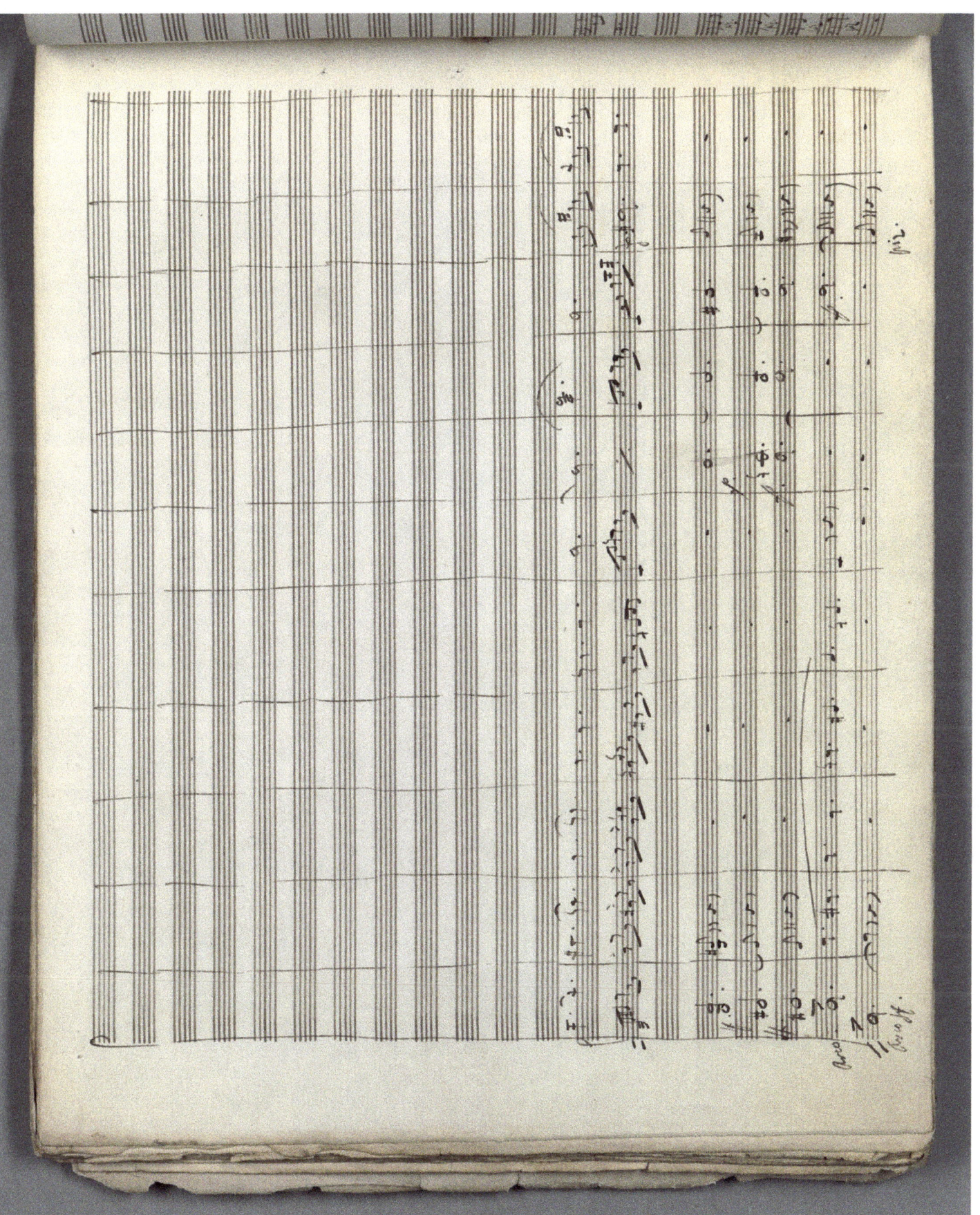

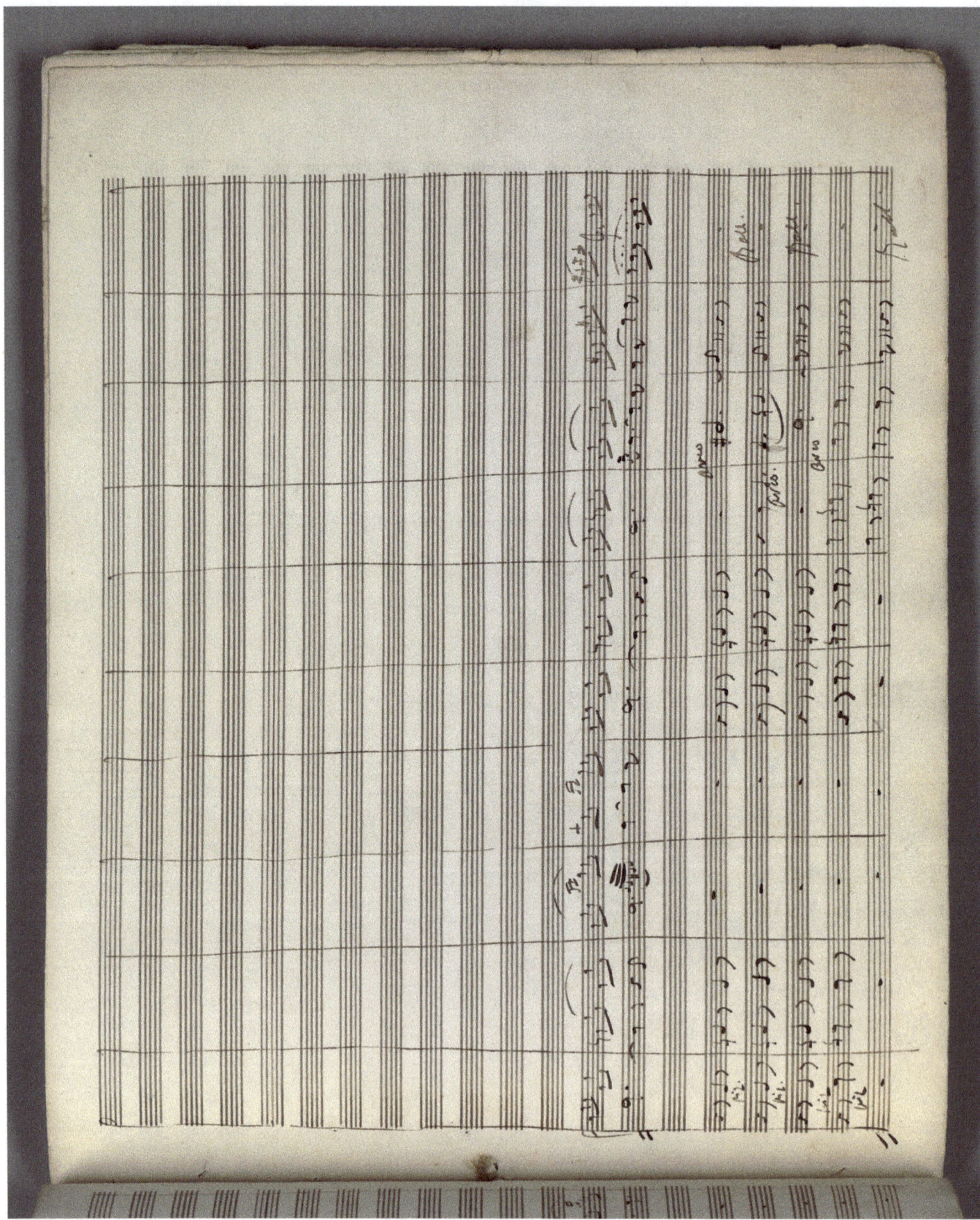

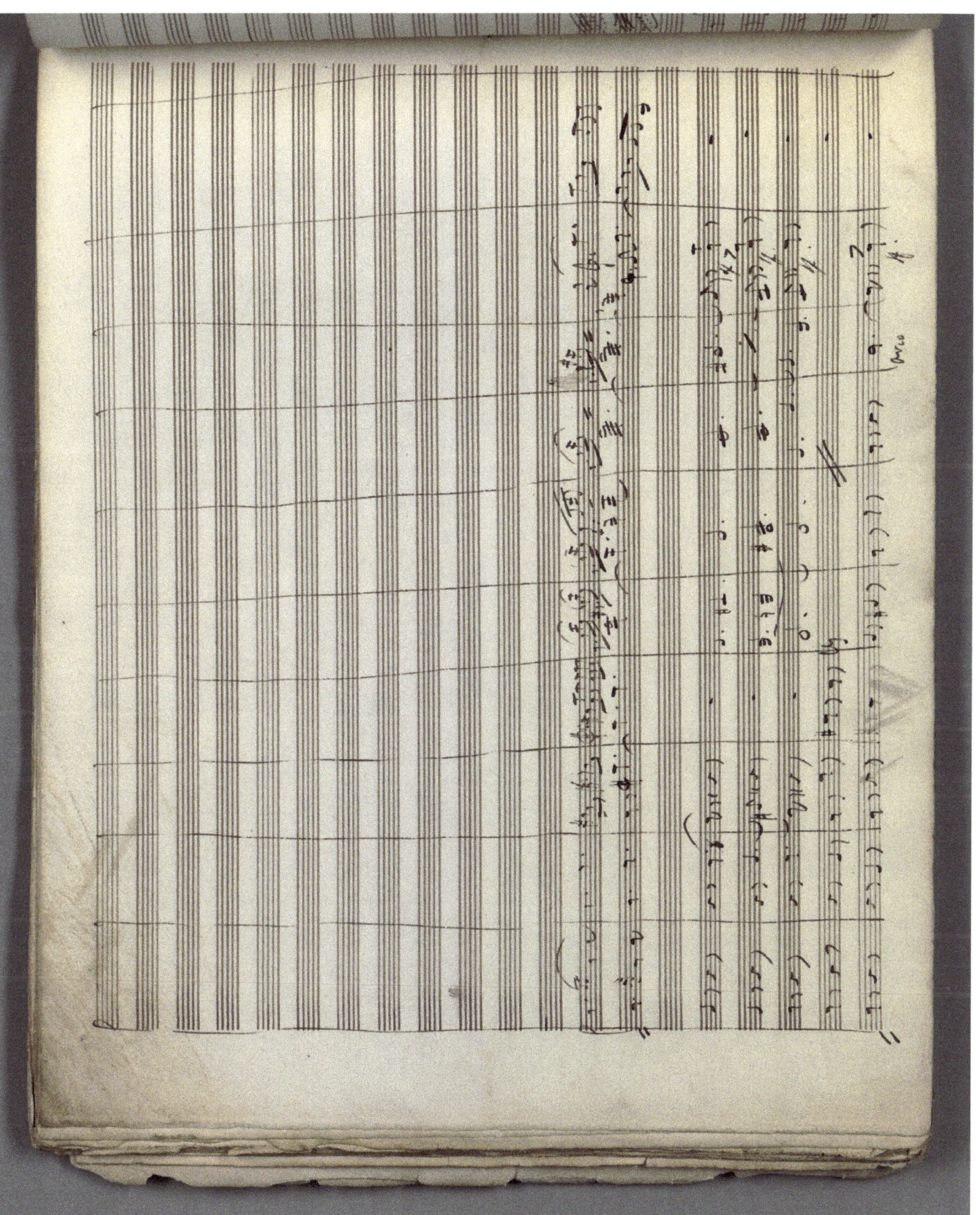

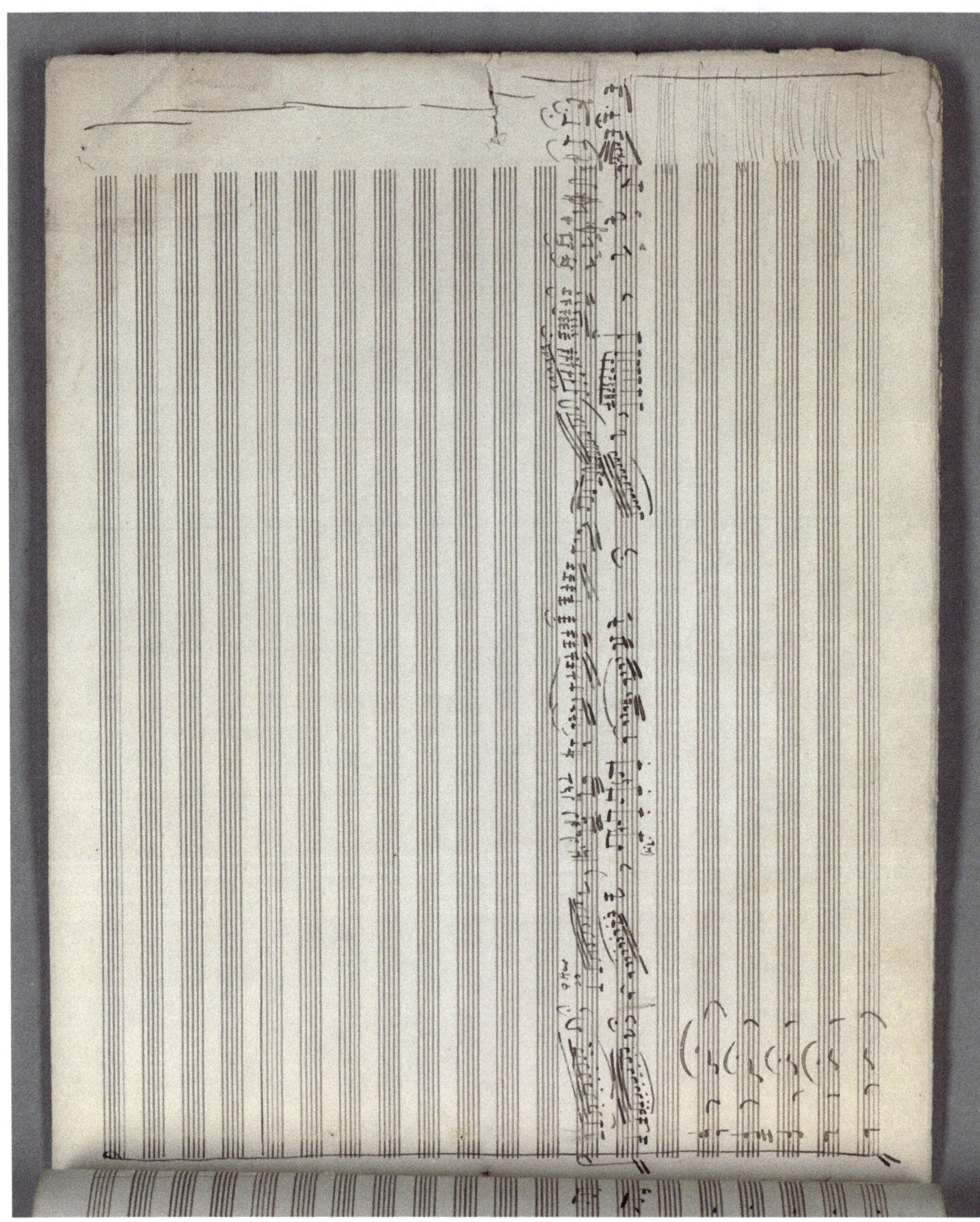

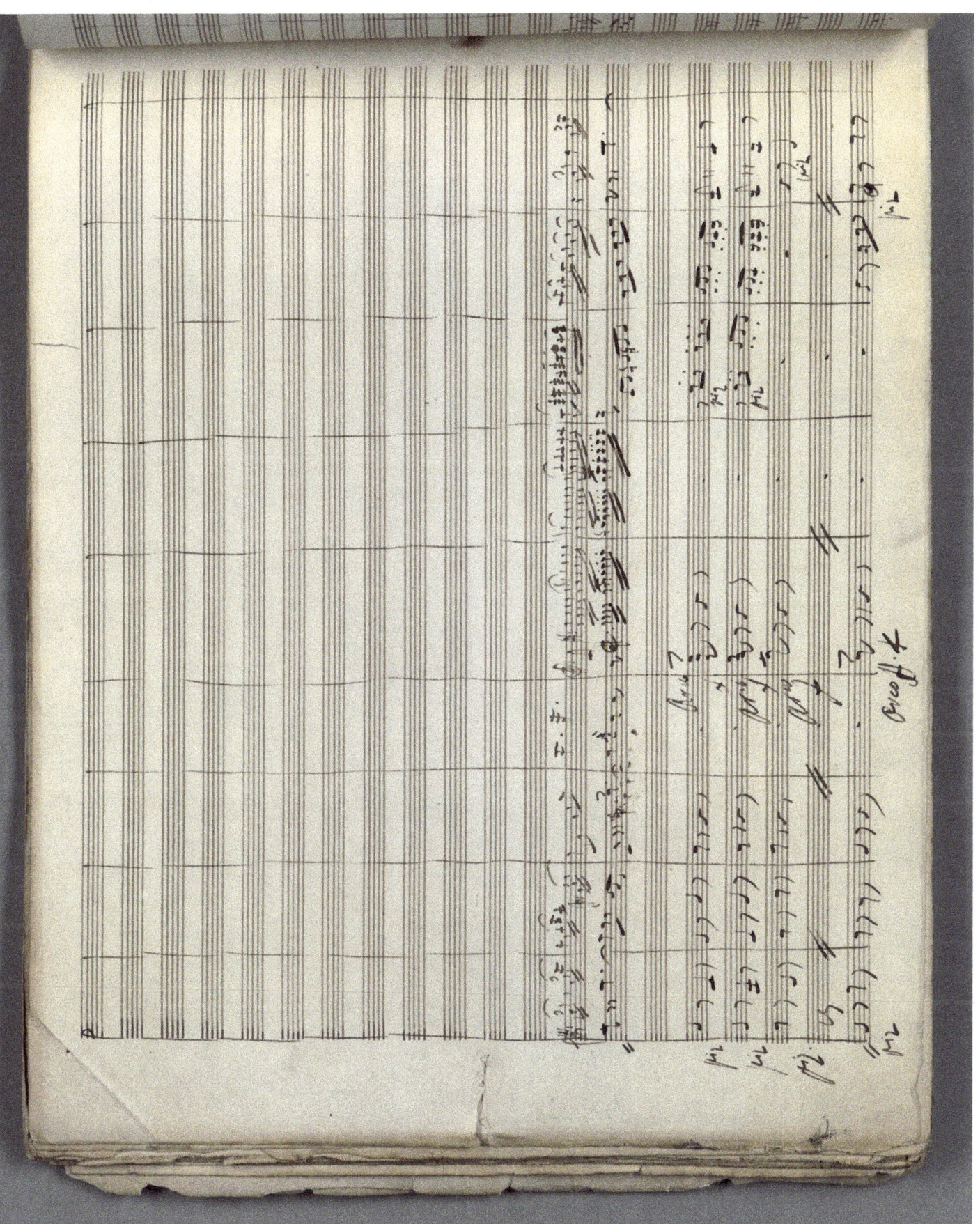

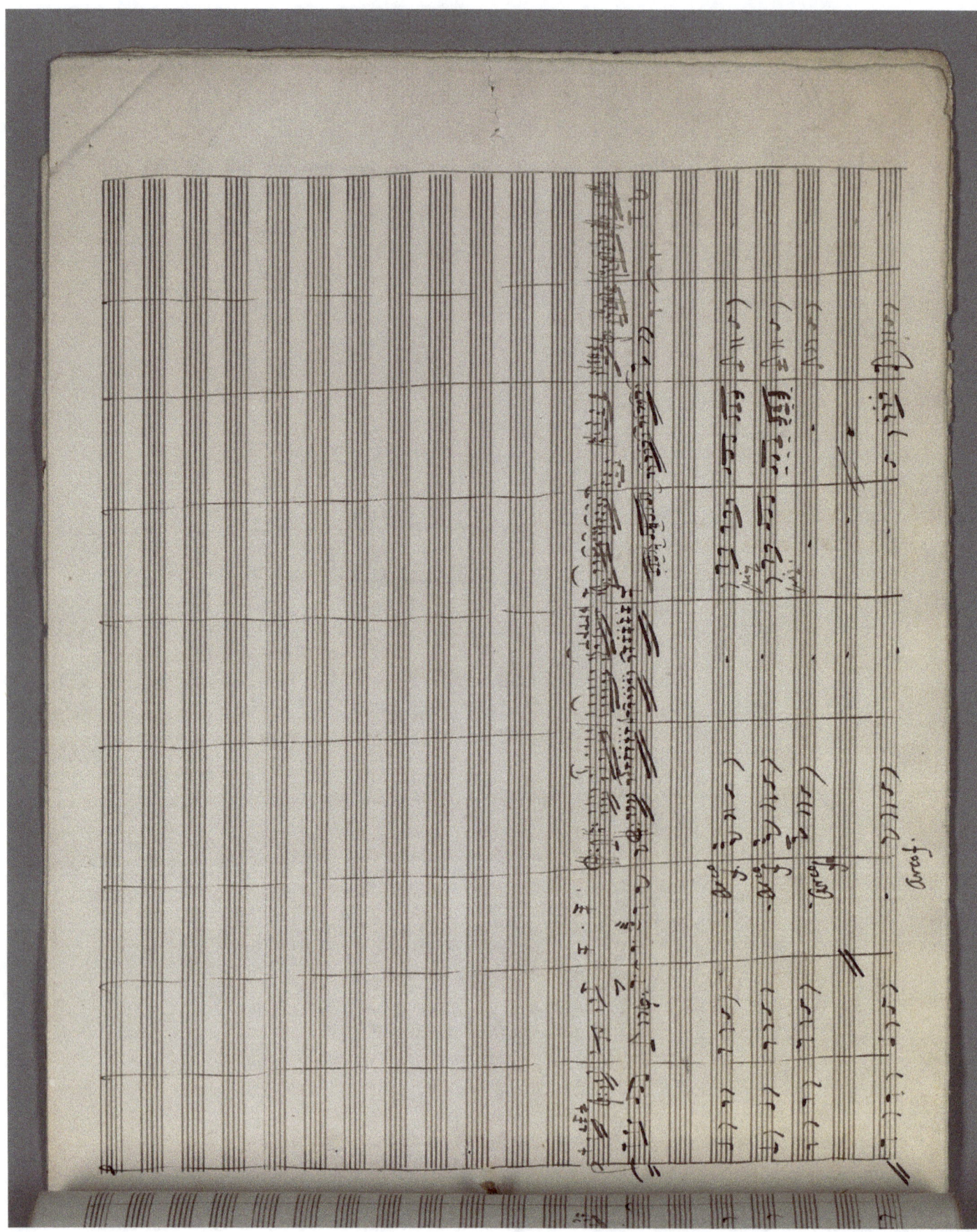

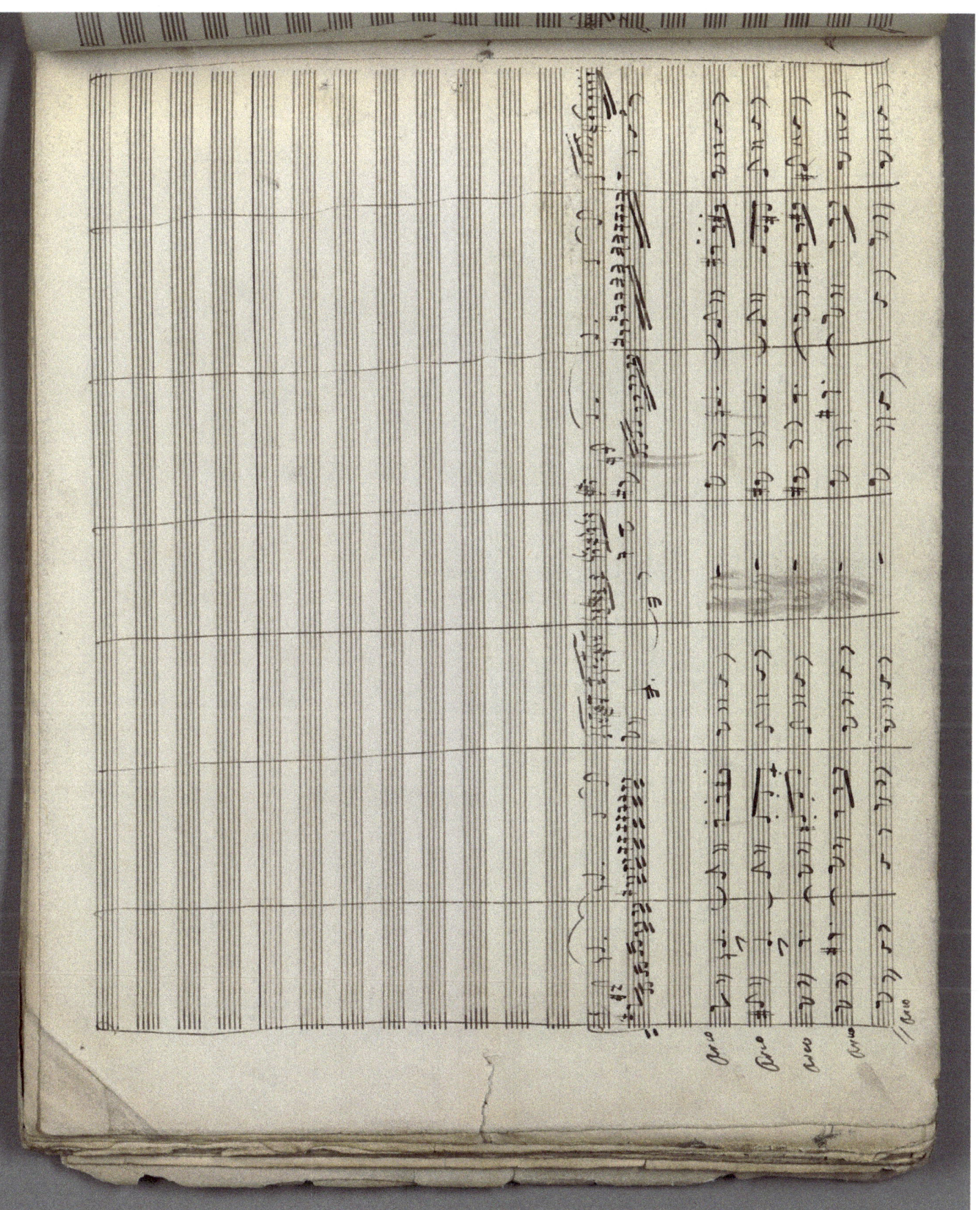

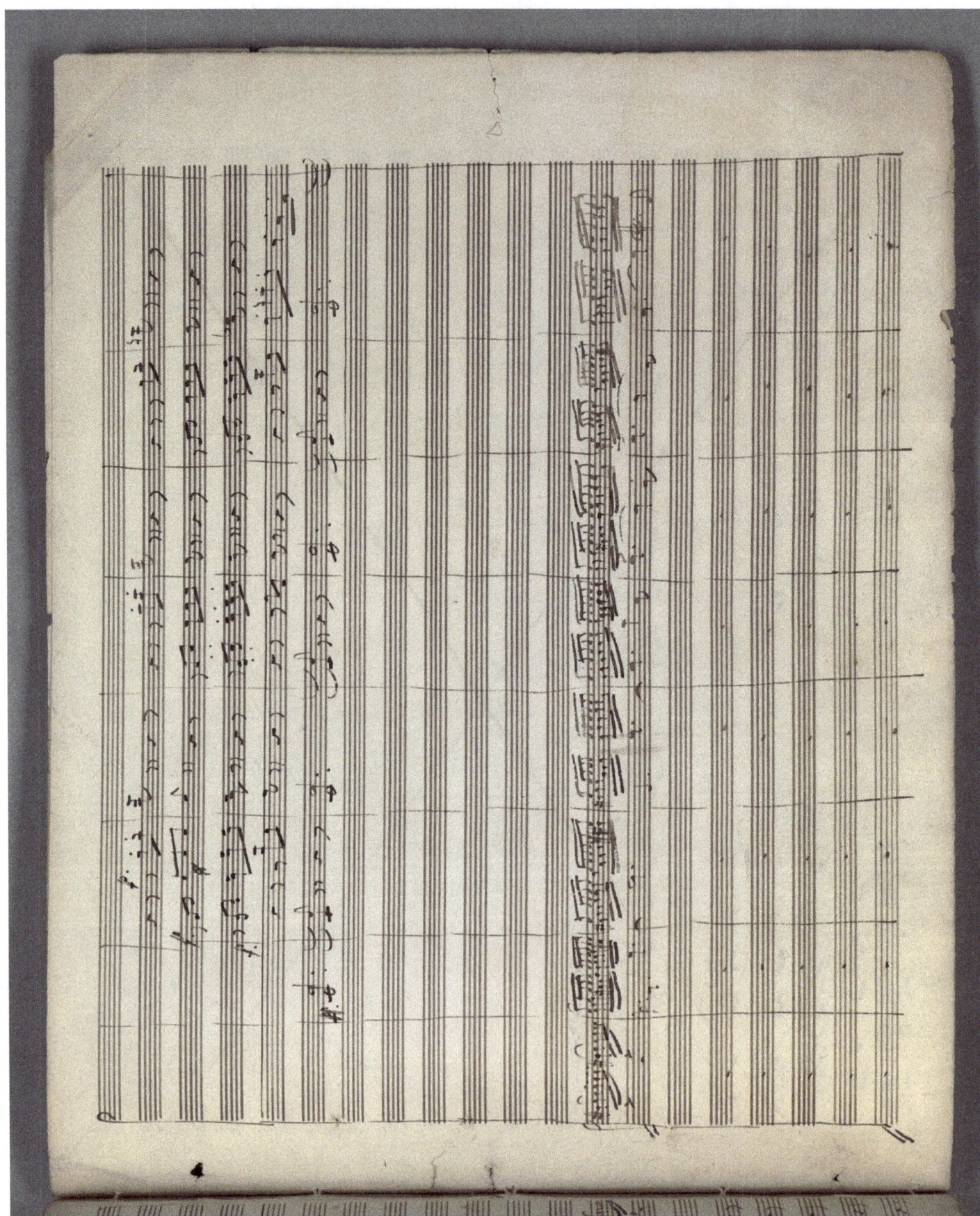

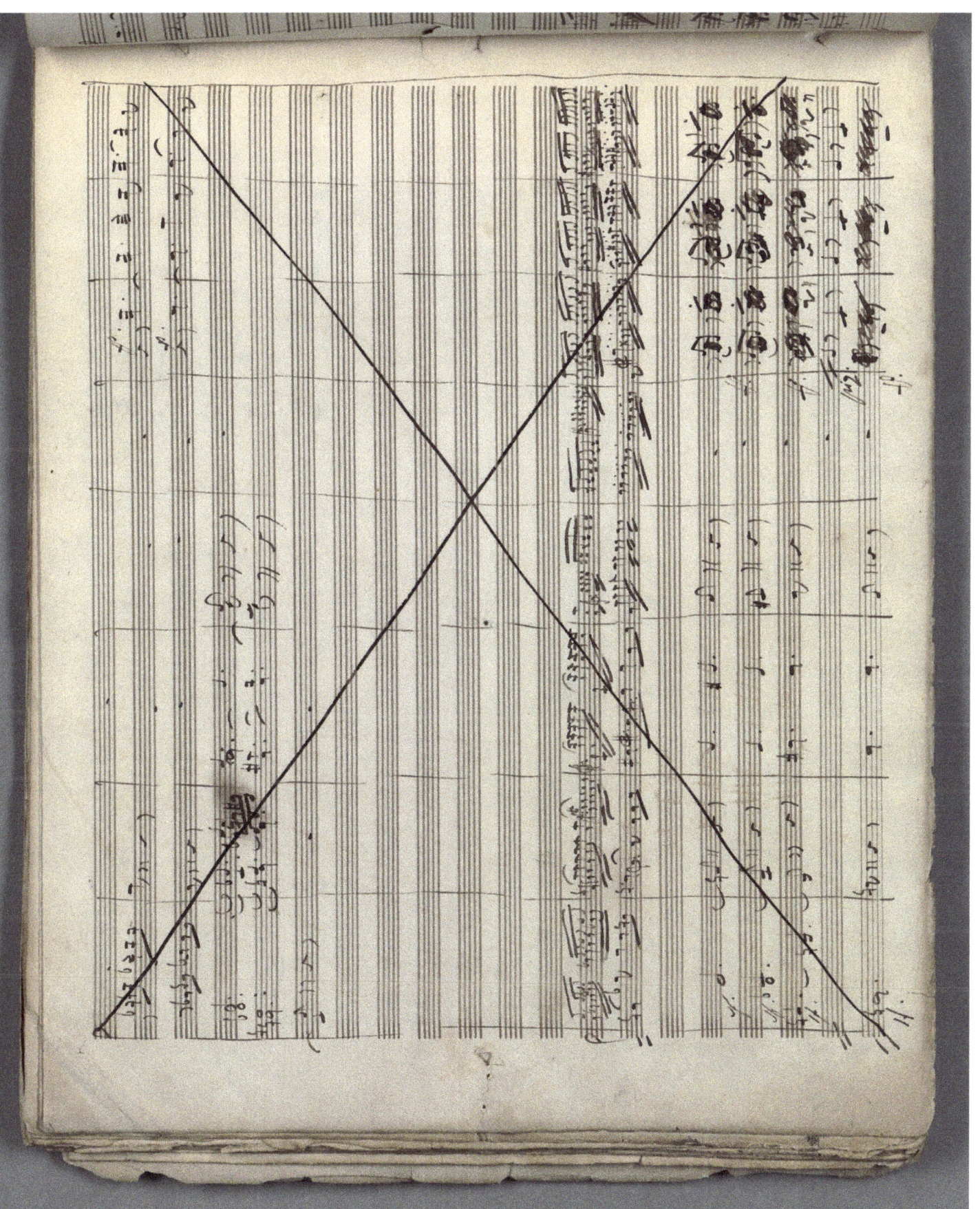

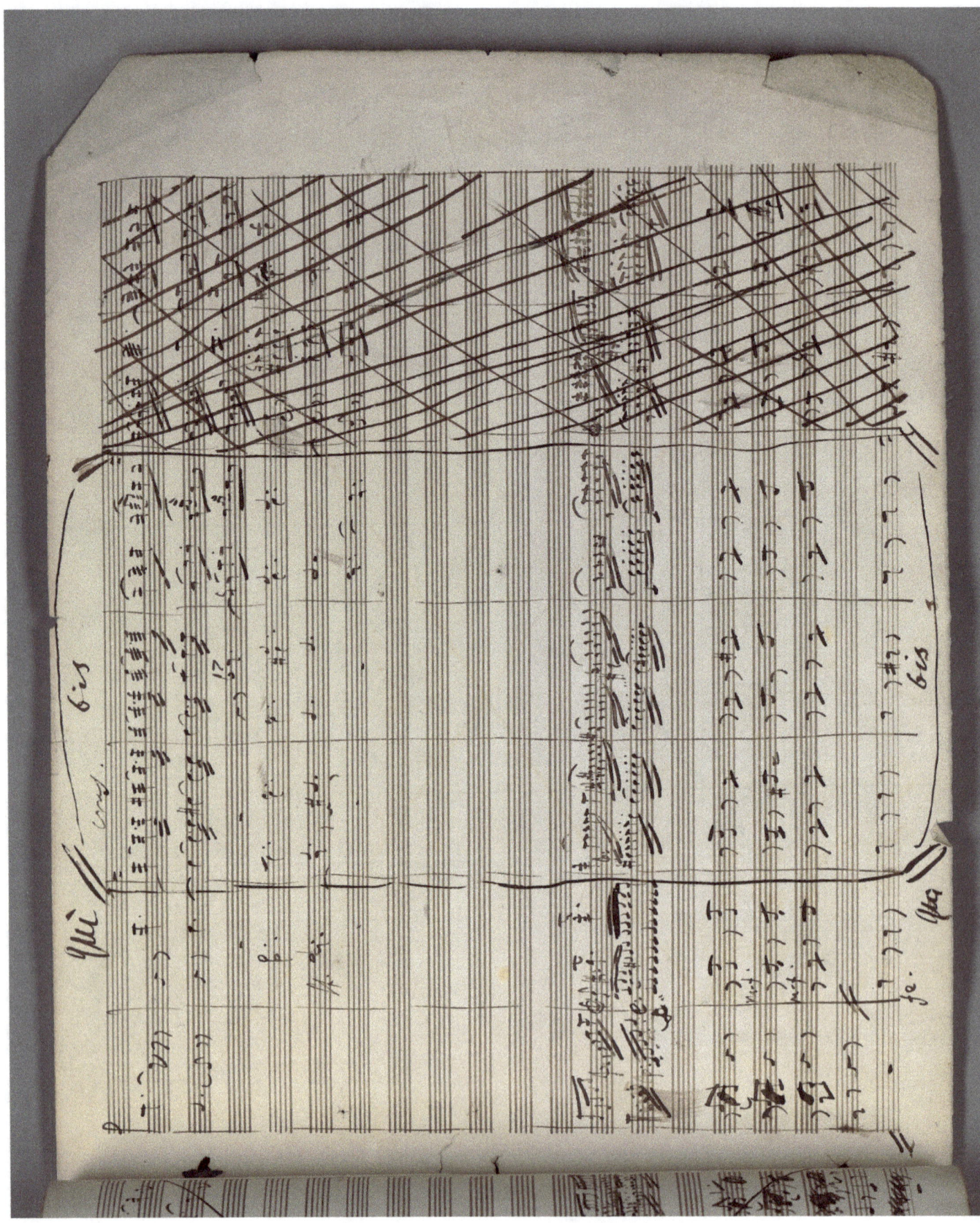

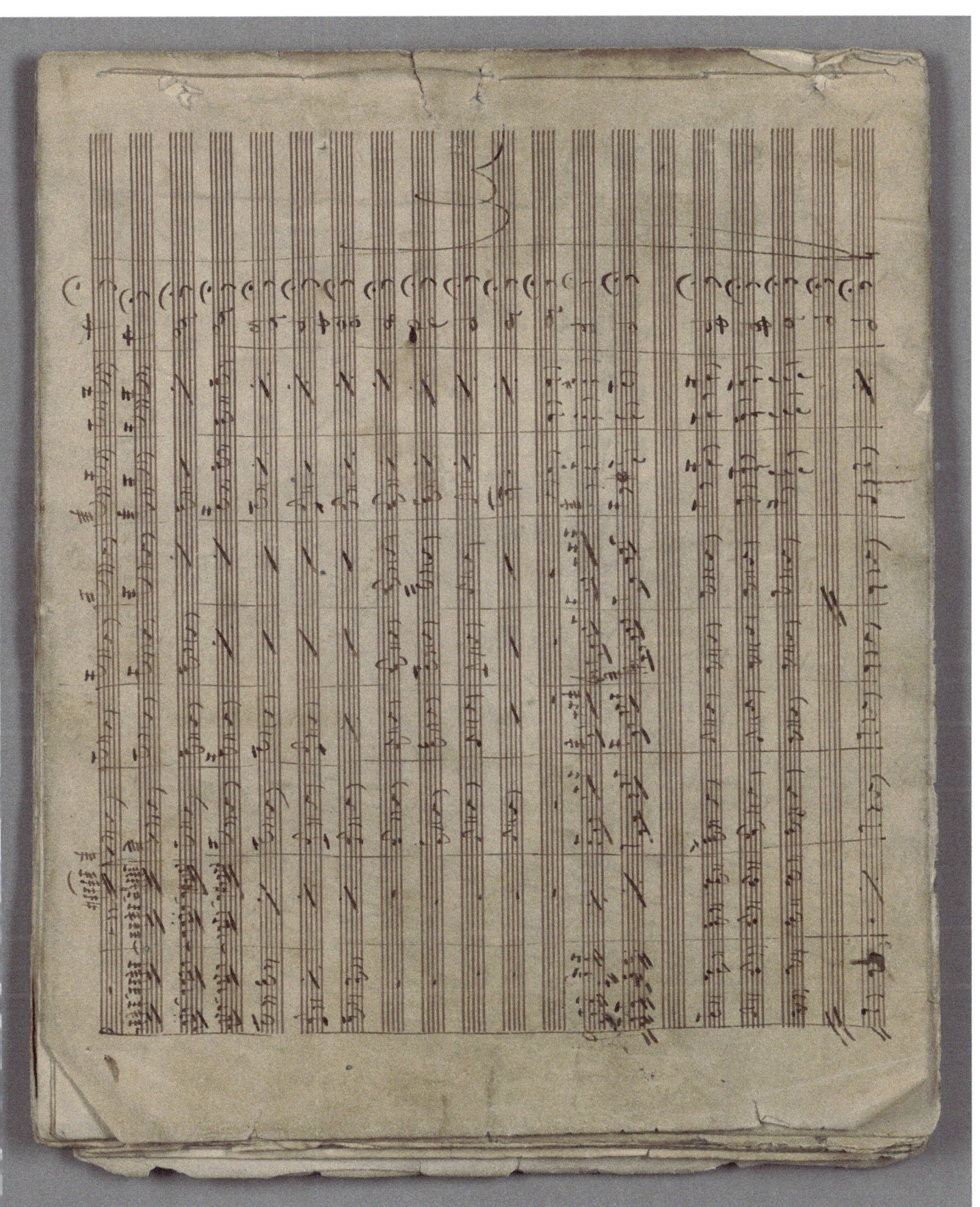

Full Score (Urtext)

Giovanni Bottesini (1821-1889)
Alfredo Piatti (1822-1901)
Vincenzo Bellini (1801-1835)

Fantasia

sopra motivi dell'Opera

I Puritani
(Bellini)

Duetto per Violoncello e Contrabbasso

Urtext Full Score

Urtext Edition Edited By Stephen Street
Adrian Bradbury And Chris West

www.bottesiniurtext.com

© Stephen Street 2021

43

Full Score (Urtext)
(Transposing Score)
*=A difference between the autograph manuscript and the modern edition

Fantasia
sopra motivi dell'Opera
I Puritani
Duetto per Violoncello e Contrabbasso

Giovanni Bottesini (1821-1889)
Alfredo Piatti (1822-1901)
Vincenzo Bellini (1801-1835)
Urtext Edition by Stephen Street
Edited By Adrian Bradbury And Chris West

Edition Copyright 2021 © Stephen Street - Part of the Bottesini Urtext® www.bottesiniurtext.com

49

67

97

Full Score (Performer's Critical Edition - Modern Instrumentation)

Giovanni Bottesini (1821-1889)
Alfredo Piatti (1822-1901)
Vincenzo Bellini (1801-1835)

Fantasia

sopra motivi dell'Opera

I Puritani
(Bellini)

Duetto per Violoncello e Contrabbasso

Full Score

Performer's Critical Edition
(with modern instrumentation)

Edited By Stephen Street
Adrian Bradbury and Chris West

www.bottesiniurtext.com

© Stephen Street 2021

Fantasia
sopra motivi dell'Opera
I Puritani
Duetto per Violoncello e Contrabbasso

Giovanni Bottesini (1821-1889)
Alfredo Piatti (1822-1901)
Vincenzo Bellini (1801-1835)
Edited By Stephen Street
Adrian Bradbury and Chris West

Non-Transposing Score

103

107

115

121

125

141

149

www.ingramcontent.com/pod-product-compliance
Lightning Source LLC
Chambersburg PA
CBHW082334180426

43199CB00037BA/2671